THE
ILLUSTRATED ENCYCLOPAEDIA
OF ANIMAL LIFE

THE ANIMAL KINGDOM

The strange and wonderful ways of mammals, birds, reptiles, fishes and insects. A new and authentic natural history of the wild life of the world

VOLUME 5

FREDERICK DRIMMER, M.A.
EDITOR-IN-CHIEF

GEORGE G. GOODWIN
*Associate Curator of Mammals,
The American Museum of Natural
History*

CHARLES M. BOGERT
*Curator of Amphibians and Reptiles,
The American Museum of Natural
History*

**DEAN AMADON
E. THOMAS GILLIARD**
*Associate Curators of Birds,
The American Museum of Natural History*

CHRISTOPHER W. COATES *Curator*
JAMES W. ATZ *Assistant Curator*
*Aquarium of the New York Zoological
Society*

JOHN C. PALLISTER
Research Associate, Insects, The American Museum of Natural History

ODHAMS BOOKS LIMITED, LONG ACRE, LONDON

HOW THE GREAT PANDA EATS

For feeding on the fibrous bamboo, the panda has developed exceedingly large and broad molar teeth, with tremendous grinding and crushing power. Strong jaw muscles also help out. But the teeth still show us this animal is a carnivore, and suggest that the pandas of ages past were substantial eaters of flesh. Those of today may now and then dine on the smaller animals in the forests of China. In a zoo, when bamboo is not available, the panda will thrive well on vegetables, cereals, cod-liver oil, and milk.

On each of its front paws the panda has a pad—the animal's scientific title, *Ailuropoda*, means "cat feet". The panda can use these pads like thumbs in bringing food to its mouth.

DELIGHTFUL CLOWN OF THE ZOO

In the zoo, the giant panda is always a star attraction. Its amusing white face with the black eye patches and its shaggy, rotund body give it great appeal; the animal is familiar to thousands of children because it has so often been copied by toy makers. In the wild state, the giant panda lives a secluded life in the remote forests of Tibet. The creature is a relative of the raccoon, and its ancestors once dwelt in the New World.

They weigh only a few pounds at birth, but by the end of their first year may reach sixty pounds or more. Because the pandas keep to themselves and are shy, quiet creatures in the wild, it is hard to find out much about them.

EAL/5—A

Since its introduction to the western world in 1937, the giant panda has been an overwhelming favourite with zoo visitors. To the delight of countless spectators—and its own delight, too—this engaging buffoon never fails to indulge its insatiable desire to perform in the broadest comedy, even of the slapstick variety. It is a pity that the panda, like many bears, tends to grow sullen and bad-tempered with age.

LESSER PANDAS—THEY LIVE HIGH UP

The Lesser Panda, or "Cat Bear", *Ailurus*, sits up on its hind legs and strikes out with its fore paws like a bear. It climbs like a bear and, when irritated, it makes the same sudden rush as the bear. It even emits the same kind of cry. But how different this little Oriental is from a bear!

The lesser panda (we must call it that to distinguish it from its big relative, the giant panda) is only about two feet long—roughly the size of a large house cat. Long, luxuriant fur, ruby red or deep chestnut in colour, covers its lithe body. The watchful face, in which two lustrous little eyes shine, is white, but a narrow dark stripe runs from the eyes to the corners of the mouth, adding to the animal's wistful charm.

Nearly straight out behind it the lesser panda carries a handsome bushy tail, about sixteen inches long and ringed with bands, alternately dark and light, that put us in mind of the raccoon. There are short claws at the end of its rather stubby legs. The animal can partly draw these claws in, so they are known as semi-retractile. With its good looks and friendly manner, the lesser panda is one of the most attractive and appealing members of the animal kingdom, especially when it has become settled in a zoo and accustomed to people.

We find the lesser panda in the forest-clad Himalayas of northern India and in western China, at elevations of seven thousand to twelve thousand feet. Slow and awkward on the ground, the animal is a first-class climber and spends much of its time in the trees. Although it may eat some insects, mice, and other small animals, its food consists mostly of vegetable matter like bamboo shoots, leaves, and fruit. The lesser panda prefers to make its den in a hollow tree, where it bears one or two young in a litter.

The Weasel and its Family—Minks, Martens, Polecats, Sables, Badgers, Skunks, and Otters

FEW ANIMAL families are more important to us than this colourful group. It contains some of our most valuable fur-bearers—the marten, the sable, the mink, and the otter. All are beasts of prey that render man great service by keeping in check the rodents, his rivals for possession of the earth.

The mustelids, as we call the members of this family (Mustelidae), include the smallest of all flesh-eaters, the weasel. Symbol of furtiveness, this little animal is none the less one of the most ferocious mammals on the face of the earth. It will attack creatures many times its size, including people, and will fight to the death. For centuries, too, the lowly weasel has been associated with royalty. The fur of the white weasel, known as ermine, or miniver, is as much a part of British coronations as the royal crown; it provided the trimming on the train of the robes Elizabeth II wore on the day she became Queen.

Members of the weasel family are found all over the world, except in New Guinea and the Australian region. Many, like the weasel, stay on the ground. But some, such as the marten, have climbed into the trees, while others—the badger is an example—burrow in the earth. A number are good swimmers: the mink and the otter hunt in and along the watercourses. All these carnivores are medium or small in size and the female is not so large as the male. They have scent-producing glands, though not always so effective as the skunk's.

WEASELS—SMALL BUT STRONG

The Ermine, *Mustela erminea*, is the most sought after of all the weasels because of the soft and luxurious white coat it wears in winter.

In the summer, however, it looks like a different animal. Then its garb varies from yellowish brown to chocolate brown. But, warm season or cold, it always wears a black tip to its tail.

The ermine seldom changes from its brown summer coat to its white winter coat before the first snow. But a long autumn without snow may retard the change, and early snows hasten it. Although the transformation is a rapid one, it is no overnight affair: it may take from ten days to three weeks. The ermine does not merely alter in the pigment or colour of its hair, but gradually sheds, or moults, the old coat, whereupon new, denser fur grows. (This white phase, we shall see, is typical of the northern weasels in general, which are then loosely called "ermine" in both the Old World and the New.)

Once the change is made, the ermine remains white until the spring moult; then it changes back to the brown coat. When a spell of warm weather in midwinter melts the snow and leaves the ground bare, the white weasel's camouflage is no longer a help, but a dangerous handicap. The animal continues to move about on top of the ground as if it were quite confident that its white body did not stand out in sharp contrast to the brown background. The ermine's enemies cannot fail to see such a public inviation to dinner.

——THE ERMINE'S ENEMIES. Ermine are killed by most hawks and owls, as well as house cats. In Connecticut the author chased a Cooper's hawk that was carrying something in its claws; it soon dropped the excess weight, which turned out to be a freshly killed ermine. At Hamilton Bay in Ontario, Canada, Ernest Thompson Seton knew a youth who shot a bald eagle which had the bleached skull of a weasel attached to its throat.

These are not the only animals the ermine must seek to elude, summer or winter. All the larger flesh-eaters, including the snakes, hunt it down.

——RELENTLESS KILLERS. In their turn the weasels (of which the ermine is typical) take an almost unbelievable toll of animal life. They are without exception the most bloodthirsty, relentless slayers among the smaller mammals. A weasel not only kills to eat, but literally kills for the sake of killing. It destroys not just smaller animals and animals its own size, but also some that are many times larger. Normally it eats only red meat soaked in hot blood.

So fierce a creature must inevitably play a major part in controlling the great hordes of rodents in its homeland, the Northern Hemisphere.

The ever-multiplying ranks of the despoilers and disease carriers, the rats and mice, would quickly overrun the earth were it not for the insatiable, tireless weasel.

This courageous little carnivore enters the dens of rats to fight and kill whole colonies, destroying them to the last individual before it will eat its hard-earned repast. It also preys upon rabbits, another serious pest.

Now and then it will raid a chicken coop, and this behaviour has given the animal a bad name. But let there be no "Weasel words" about it—to man the weasel is more friend than foe.

Although the ermine, like other weasels, spends most of its time on the ground, it can swim; often, too, it climbs trees in search of bird nests to rob. Sometimes it may have another purpose in going aloft. The nest of a female ermine has been found in a hole of a tree trunk, fourteen feet above the ground. In typical weasel fashion, the nest was lined with rabbit fur. In it lay the head of a rabbit. The ermine must have had a difficult job hauling the head up the steep side of the tree. But the prospect of work or war seldom daunts a member of the weasel tribe.

——ERMINE AT PLAY. Ermine have their playful moods, too. At times, several will perform in a most amazing manner. They roll over each other, twist, turn, and spar with each other. Often they will spring four feet in the air and turn as perfect a somersault as any boy at play. In this gay mood the ermine utters a chuckling, happy sound in a high or a low key. (When it is angry, you will hear a loud, chattering noise from it.)

——HUNGRY BABIES. The ermine and other northern weasels usually mate in July or August, but the babies do not come until the following March or April. The den, or nursery, is a hole in the ground or under a rock (the former rat or rabbit occupant having been slain by the new tenants). There are from six to twelve young in a litter (seven or eight is average). Since each baby consumes more than half its weight in food every day, it would hardly be possible for the mother to supply the family needs without the aid of the father. Not only do both parents take an active part in caring for the young; we sometimes find a year-round association of the male and female.

The baby ermine, like so many other carnivores, is blind at birth. It weighs under two grammes, is flesh coloured, and has a fine, downy covering of white hair. It does not open its eyes until about thirty-five days have passed. In another week it goes on a meat diet, but remains under parental care until August. Highly strung animals, continually on the move, and apparently indefatigable, the ermine reach old age in seven or eight years.

——WHERE WE FIND THEM. In adulthood, American ermine average about eight inches in head-and-body length, with a three-inch tail; they do not weigh much more than three or four ounces. Their range extends from the Arctic to northern Connecticut and the Great Lakes in the eastern states and about five degrees farther south in the Rocky Mountains. We find a number of different-named varieties in Europe and northern Asia, and these are about twice as large as their American cousins and belong in the same genus. (In its brown summer coat, the European ermine is popularly known as the stoat.)

All in all, we may observe that the ermine's range covers pretty much the region of heavy snowfall in the Northern Hemisphere, a fact that has been extremely significant in the animal's development.

Why Some Weasels Are White in Winter. We have suggested that the underlying reason for the remarkable whitening of the winter coat of the ermine (or, for that matter, of the weasels that we generally find in the northern part of the world) is protective coloration. These weasels are always white where snow lies deep on the ground all the winter and every winter.

Where there is never, or rarely, any snow, weasels are brown in winter. The colour change, where there is one, is effected by a moult in the autumn and one in the spring, as we have seen. But even the weasels that are brown in winter undergo the same two annual moults. These animals change coats, although not colours.

The change from a brown summer to a white winter coat is hereditary. A brown weasel—from an area where no seasonal changes in colour take place—if kept in the north where there is deep snow, would still be brown, winter after winter. If a white weasel (one born and reared in the north) is transferred to the south where there is no snow, it will continue to turn white every winter. The change, we perceive, is a calendar routine; neither snow nor temperature is the direct cause.

Until recently, the mechanism of the colour changes was a mystery. Now we know they are actually determined by the amount of light. As the days get shorter in the autumn, the weasel receives less light through its eyes. This causes the pituitary gland to stop producing a substance known as gonadotropic hormones. The lack of these hormones deprives the hair cells of pigment, and the new hair growing under such conditions is of course white.

In the spring, the story is exactly the opposite. The nights get shorter. The increasing amount of light coming through the eyes of the weasel now stimulates the pituitary gland and increases the pigment in the hair cells, which gives colour to the hair in the spring moult.

EXCEEDINGLY ALERT AND WARY

The weasel is the smallest of the flesh-eaters, but what it lacks in size it makes up in ferocity. This short-legged beast hunts by scent and is a relentless killer of mice, rats, moles, rabbits, and poultry. Northern weasels wear a snow-white coat in winter, a brown one in other seasons.

A white weasel kept in a dark place would have a tendency to stay white through lack of light, but because of heredity would change to brown with the spring moult or white with the autumn moult.

Colour changes in other animals like the snowshoe rabbit are effected in a similar manner. It is interesting to note that cave-dwelling animals that live in almost total darkness, such as fish and salamanders, are often white. These same creatures would have colour if they lived in the light. Some late-flying bats that roost in dark caves are also white. Most of the animals we find in the Arctic regions, where the light is never strong, are white: examples are the Arctic fox, the polar bear, the snowy owl, and the white gyrfalcons.

The Long-tailed Weasel, *Mustela frenata,* is the common species of the weasel and the one usually seen in most parts of the United States, where it takes the place of the ermine; its range extends from the Great Lakes in Canada to Ecuador and Peru in South America.

This animal's typical colour is deep reddish brown, graduating to almost black. The tropical American weasel has on its face a white marking in the form of a bridle—"bridled weasel" is actually the meaning of its scientific name. Only in the northern part of its range does the long-tailed weasel turn white in winter. Then people often refer to it as an ermine, though it is really another species.

The long-tailed weasel seems to prefer more open country than its shorter-tailed, more northern cousin. We find it in regions where there is an abundance of small animal life upon which it can feed. In search of food it may cover several miles in a single day, but usually it moves about in an area of not more than fifteen acres.

THE DOMESTIC SCENE

Little Bridle-Face's home life is like that of the other weasels. It lives in a shallow burrow in the ground. The den is usually some six inches or so below the surface and the nest chamber about ten or twelve inches in diameter. It provides a fine warm lining for the nest —chiefly the fur of its victims.

June or July is the mating season for the long-tailed weasels, as a rule. There is a period of delayed development of the embryos as with all weasels, and babies are born from 220 to 337 days after mating time. The weasel mother has from four to eight young in her litter. They will average about three grammes each when a day old—no substantial weight when you consider that a cigarette weighs about a gramme. In two weeks they are clothed in a silky white coat.

By the time the young weasels open their eyes (on the thirty-sixth or thirty-seventh day) they are well on the road to maturity: these "babies" are weaned when five or six weeks old and fully grown at ten weeks. Naturalists who have studied the long-tailed weasel closely, claim that both parents work together in caring for the young, and this would indicate pairing for life.

The weight of full-grown males may reach six ounces, while the head and body generally span about ten inches. The tail may measure about six inches in length. Is that really long? Only in comparison with other weasels' tails, and so we call this one the long-tailed weasel.

There are many forms of long-tailed weasels, including the well-known New York Weasel, but all are sub-species of *Mustela frenata*. The bridled weasel is the one you are most likely to encounter in South and Central America.

The Short-tailed Weasel, or Snow Weasel, *Mustela nivalis*, a common animal in the Old World, is a creature for which the author has a special affection. As a boy, in England, he made a pet of one. When he found it, it was only a baby, having been dropped by its fleeing mother. He fed the tiny weasel on warm milk until it was able to eat raw meat. Gentle and friendly, it never lost its amiable disposition and loved to hide inside the author's shirt for warmth.

However, a full-grown male that the author caught in a mole runway had an entirely different temperament. This weasel lived on in captivity for six months, but never did it change its ferocious nature. The animal remained savage and intractable, permitting no one to pet it, and would attempt to sink its teeth into any moving object that came near. Such behaviour is typical of its kind.

——An Animal of Great Rapacity. The short-tailed weasel feeds primarily on mice; it may also climb low shrubbery to stalk birds. It has larders in crevices and holes in trees in which it stores food. What a good supply of meat this hungry little butcher keeps! One such storehouse was found to contain three wrens, one goldcrest, one chaffinch, one mouse, two pigeon heads, one pigeon leg, and other remains unidentifiable.

Those who know this beast well, have many anecdotes to relate concerning its tenaciousness, courage, and rapacity. For example, more than one dog has retrieved a rabbit to which a short-tailed weasel was still clinging, unwilling to loosen its hold on the prey's throat.

On one occasion a kestrel was seen to rise a good thirty feet in the air and let something drop; it turned out to be a dead rat with a weasel hanging to it. Few records of dauntlessness can equal these.

Call a person a weasel, to suggest that he is cowardly or a sneak? That would hardly be doing justice to the fearless weasel.

——"DANDY DOGS". According to tradition, the short-tailed weasel travels and hunts in company after dark. This may well tie in with a superstition that still lingers in the West of England to the effect that hares are hunted at night by packs of little fairy hounds known as "dandy dogs". The local country folk will assure you that they have watched them with awe.

The author has found sufficient evidence to prove that the weasel often travels and hunts in packs of up to eight individuals. However, it is generally one family that is involved.

——SMALL ENOUGH TO ENTER MOLE RUNWAYS. No need to guess where the short-tailed weasel gets its name. The tail (which lacks the black tip characteristic of many other species) is only two and one-half inches long; the rest of the animal may be eight inches. This weasel is small enough to enter underground burrows; it has turned up in the author's mole traps, caught as it travelled along the runways of the garden mole in search of prey.

The short-tailed weasel makes its home in Great Britain (where it is called a weasel, as opposed to a stoat or ermine), Europe and Asia; we encounter related forms in Egypt and on the islands of the Mediterranean. The short-tail has brown fur, but, like its long-tailed relatives in the New World, it will wear a white winter coat in the northern part of its range.

The Least or Pygmy Weasel, *Mustela rixosa*, is the smallest of the weasel tribe. It is only about six inches long, and has a one-inch tail with hardly a trace of the usual black tip. In summer this little fellow is a uniform reddish brown on the upper parts, and white below; in winter it is an unbroken white.

No wide-roaming hunter is the pygmy weasel. It has a maximum home range of about two acres and seldom travels far from its burrow in the ground. However, having cleared one area of mice, it moves on to another.

When the pygmy settles in a new locality, it selects a mouse's nest in some concealed place either on the surface or, more often, underground. It immediately starts to line the nest with hair plucked from its victims. The pygmy will carry mice into the den and consume them there. Sometimes it will store them in connecting galleries.

The pygmy differs from its relatives in that it has no fixed breeding season. Its young may be born in any month of the year, but spring and winter seem to be the commonest times. The average litter contains four or five babies; however, there may be up to ten.

The homeland of the pygmy is the northern regions of the earth. We find the animal spread across Europe (except Britain) and east as far as Siberia. In North America it is present from Alaska south to Nebraska and, in the eastern United States, in the Allegheny Mountains of Pennsylvania. In Alaska it is highly regarded by the Indians, who view the capture of the least weasel as a piece of good fortune. One old Indian claimed that his brother, who had caught one when he was a child, had in consequence become a "big chief".

The Kolinsky, *Mustela siberica,* the large yellow weasel of north-eastern Asia, is perhaps better known dyed and made up into a fur coat than as a wild animal. It got its name from Kola, a district in north-eastern Russia, where the best pelts come from. Kolinsky also goes under such names as Shantung, China mink, Japanese mink, and yellow mink. For the living animal the natives of northern China have the most picturesque name of all—they call it *huang shu lang,* meaning "yellow rat wolf".

The author caught a number of the big yellow weasels along the banks of frozen rivers in Siberia. He found them still active at temperatures 60 degrees below zero, and was surprised at their resemblance to mink in all respects except colour—even their habits were like the mink's. Although the fur lacks the luxuriant lustre of the true mink, still kolinsky is an important item in the trade.

A related species, the Alpine Weasel, lives in the high mountains of Tibet. The Java Weasel is even more minklike than the kolinsky, but, as you have probably guessed, the fur of tropical weasels is a poor grade. In northern Burma and Indo-China we find the only weasel with a striped back.

MINKS—FISHERS AND HUNTERS

The Mink, *Mustela* (*Lutreola*) *vison,* looks like a weasel, only one grown large and robust. It has the same long, supple body and short limbs. It has the same murderous habits, too, with even greater power and skill to exercise them.

This weasel-like creature can and does hunt fish. With a normal swimming rate of some two miles per hour, it catches the wily trout in fast-running streams. It can swim faster under water than a muskrat but not so far or so deep. No matter—it catches the muskrat often enough.

The mink wreaks terrific havoc among marsh birds, and young snapping turtles also fall prey to it. Like the weasel, the mink is fond of rats, mice, and rabbits, which it hunts in the woods and bushes. Unlike the weasel, it does not seem to practise killing so much for the sheer joy of it.

THE MINK'S LAIR

The mink is chiefly active at night, but you may see it about at any hour of the day. It makes its home near watercourses, on the margin between the dry land and deep water. Here an individual's territory covers an area about five miles in diameter, over which the animal ranges for its food supply. Its lair is a hollow tree, a crevice in the rocks, or a burrow dug in a river bank.

Often this carnivorous creature will carry its kill home and eat it. A mink's lair is always littered with the bones and scales of its victims. Where there is good hunting and fishing, a whole week's supply of dead fish and animals may be cached in the mink's storehouse. In one mink's den, for example, thirteen muskrats and three waterfowl were found.

RUNNING AND PLAYING

On land, the mink is not so swift as the weasel. It may gallop along with arched back or walk at a rapid, nervous pace. In a lighter frame of mind, it has been known to slide down hillsides in simple, playful fun. On one occasion a mink was seen to make eight slides, one after another, down a snowbank.

ENEMIES OF THE MINK

A mink's life is not all hunting and playing, however. The large owls sometimes swoop down upon it from the air; sometimes the lynx and the fox eat it. The stench the mink produces from its musk glands, although more potent than the weasel's, and extremely annoying to human beings, is not effective enough to drive larger enemies away. The mink will put up a good fight, however, before it is taken.

FAMILY LIFE AMONG THE MINKS

The mink mates in February and March. About a month and a half later, the litter comes, with four to eight sightless, almost naked kittens in it. They open their eyes when five weeks old, and at about this time they begin to eat solid food. The father pitches in and helps the mother to find it for them.

During their adolescent age the young are very playful—in a savage sort of way. Their games are mostly of the rough-house type;

THE MINK PATROLS LAKES AND STREAMS

The lustrous fur of the mink has such great value that the animal is now reared in large numbers on farms in the Scandinavian countries, Canada, the United States and also in Britain. Hundreds of thousands of the animals are also taken in the wild. A fierce and active creature, the mink feeds on much the same fare as the weasel, plus fish, frogs, and crayfish.

they spring and jump at each other, lose their tempers and squeal, hiss, or growl angrily. As they grow older, they begin to fight and quarrel in earnest. Now, too, they are getting big and strong enough to earn their own keep, and they follow their mother and father on hunting trips.

For most of the summer, the family remains together, hunting or frolicking. With autumn come an end and a beginning. Each of the minks goes its own way to find a new territory in which to settle. At this time of the year they often travel a considerable distance from water, cutting across wide stretches of country from one watershed to another.

MINK FUR AND FARMS

Mink fur is a staple item in the fur trade. It is fine and beautiful, with great durability and an attractive natural dark brown colour. It is perhaps the most popular fur on the market and always commands a high price.

Throughout the world, about a million mink are taken each year. So great has been the demand, that it laid the basis for a new industry, mink farming, which began almost a hundred years ago. Mink farming has released some of the pressure on the wild mink, and today over two hundred thousand ranch-raised animals are harvested annually in the United States alone, most of them in Louisiana.

MALE AND FEMALE

An adult mink (male) weighs about two pounds. It is about two feet long, and its rather bushy tail is roughly a third as long again. The soft, thick underfur is overlaid with long black glistening guard hairs, which protect the animal's coat when there is swimming to be done. It may have white spots on its chin and throat. The female is smaller but has the same colouring.

Where We Find Them. The mink is found over nearly all of North America from the Gulf of Mexico to the Arctic, and in the Old World from north-eastern Asia to Finland and from south-western France to eastern Rumania. There are a number of different geographical forms but only two living species; the American Mink, *Mustela vison*, and the European Mink, *Mustela lutreola*.

A larger species, the Sea Mink, *Mustela macrodon*, used to be found along the coast of Maine and the adjoining Canadian seashore, but it died out about one hundred years ago. Today the only relics of this animal are fragments of skulls from the Indian shell heaps at Brookline, Hancock County, Maine.

POLECATS AND FERRETS

The Common Polecat or Fitch, *Mustela putorius*, is the only member of the weasel family that has been truly domesticated. This legendary animal is about the size of an alley cat, with a bushy tail. The beautiful soft fur is uniformly buffy grey in colour, overshadowed with black-tipped hairs.

There seems to be some question as to where the polecat got its name. It could be just plain "Polish cat" but more likely it was derived from the Gaelic for "pool cat", signifying a cat that lives in a hole in the ground. The French word *poule*—it means "fowl" or "hen"—is another possibility, as the polecat is noted for robbing chicken pens.

The popular word "polecat", signifying an evil-smelling animal, originated with this animal, but formerly the name had no such meaning. The American skunk is sometimes called a polecat because of its odour.

The polecat is a home-lover and a good housekeeper. Its den is usually a hole in a well-drained dry bank or among the rocks. There is an outside toilet, a warm nest chamber (the polecat loves comfort) and a connecting runway that leads to the larder, which is kept well stocked with good things to eat. Here one may find birds, rats, rabbits, and reptiles. In one polecat's pantry were found fifty frogs and toads; all were alive, but each had been bitten through the brain and thus rendered helpless.

March and April is the time for courting, and both parents take an active interest in the family that comes forty days later. The kittens are born like so many other young animals—naked, without sight, and quite dependent. They open their eyes for the first time twenty-one days later.

Baby polecats make their first appearance in the outside world when six weeks old. They love to sport and play and in the warm sunshine they dance around each other in a most amusing manner.

At the first sign of danger, however, the little playfellows dive for home after colliding with, and falling over, each other in their terrified scramble to get safely underground. The life span of these animals is nine or ten years.

We have seen that in earlier days the polecat did not possess the reputation of being an evil-smelling creature. Attacked by dogs, or badly scared, it can, like the skunk, eject a nauseating liquid secretion from the musk glands situated at the base of the tail. But normally it makes every attempt to escape before resorting to chemical warfare. When it is kept in captivity there is no indication of an offensive odour.

——POLECAT HUNTING. Fifty years ago polecat hunting was a popular sport in the North of England. The chase, generally conducted on moonlit nights with a pack of hounds (a cross between otter hounds and fox terriers), would cover a distance of six or seven miles. In the sporting field the polecat was known as the foumart ("foul marten") to distinguish it from the sweet marten and on account of the objectionable odour it emitted when captured by the hounds.

——WHERE WE FIND IT. The polecat is at home in semi-wooded and open country in Europe, from Great Britain east to Siberia and Mongolia and south to the Himalayas. In North Africa it makes its home in the mountains of the western Rif, in Morocco. There are three species.

HUNTING WITH FERRETS

The Domesticated Polecat, *Mustela furo* ("weasel thief"), is the common ferret. It is well known in Europe, but has scarcely been heard of in America. Because they possess long, slender bodies and a keen desire to kill, ferrets are used to drive rabbits and rats out of their holes so that they can be shot, or killed by dogs.

Ferreting has been a popular sport in Europe for several centuries, but it is known to have been practised in Asia as early as the first century before Christ.

The ancient tribes of that continent selected the smaller wild species, *Mustela eversmanni*, for their purpose. It has since been crossed with the larger European polecat, but in the selective breeding of ferrets the smaller polecats are used. Ferreting was also a common sport with the Romans. Strabo states that ferrets were originally brought from

Michigan Conservation Department

THIS FERRET FORAGES FOR ITSELF

Hunting with ferrets has been a popular sport in Europe for centuries and was practised in Asia before 100 B.C. However "hunting" ferrets are the domesticated product of cross-breeding the original European ferrets and small polecats, and about the only thing they have in common with the American black-footed ferret is their membership of the weasel family. Big for a weasel, the black-foot has the typical long, slender, short-legged body and a thick coat of sleek, soft, tawny and black fur. Its natural food supply dwindling, the handsome independent animal has joined the lamentably large group of vanishing American species. See *page 507.*

THE "BADGE" OF THE BADGER

While the facial markings of American badgers differ slightly from those of their widespread Eurasian counterparts, there is no mistaking the family connection. Fully grown, these pups will be a little smaller than the Eurasian varieties but will lack none of their courage and determination. The American badger ranges westward from the Great Lakes region, south to Mexico, north to British Columbia, making its home in the plains, prairies and deserts. See *page 520.*

Wisconsin Conservation Department

"ALASKA SABLE"

The striped skunk's glossy coat of long, limp hair is much in demand in the fur trade and the amiable little animal, fully aware of its understandable lack of natural enemies, is not very wary and is easily trapped. The exceptional adaptability of these house cat sized members of the weasel group to all sorts of environment helps maintain the species throughout the North American continent. While the black and white pattern may vary, it is outlined on the pink skin of the newborn skunk almost as though tattooed. See page 524.

L. L. Rue

MASTER OF DEFENSIVE CHEMICAL WARFARE

As long as the very tip of the tail hangs limp, the intruder—who has already been warned away by growling and foot stamping—can still beat a strategic retreat, but once the tip goes up he is in imminent danger of a malodorous drenching. Smallest of the three American species, the spotted skunk is no less well-equipped with the universally respected defence mechanism, and no less adept in its use. See page 524.

L.L. Rue

[5-1]

Long slender body, short legs, flattened head and low, rounded ears are typical of the weasel. Despite its small size it is the most bloodthirsty of all mammals, often killing merely for the sake of killing. *See page 493*

The species of weasel known as ermine is most glamorous in winter when its coat has changed from brown to snow-white with the tip of the tail remaining black. The changing of colour may be completed in ten days or may require as long as three weeks. *See page 493*

[5-1A]

[5-2]

Larger and more robust than the weasel, the mink resembles it not only in appearance but murderous habits, although it restricts its killing more to food gathering. An excellent swimmer, the mink will lay aside a considerable store of fish when the supply is plentiful.   *See page 501*

Old World ferrets have been cared for by humans for so long they are completely dependent and cannot survive if lost, but the American black-footed ferret is an entirely different animal. Prairie dog country is its home and as the little rodents, its principal source of food, become more scarce, the ferret is threatened with extinction.   *See page 507*

[5-2A]

NATIONAL AUDUBON SOCIETY

Africa to Spain; Pliny was familiar with the sport in his day and refers to it as being practised in hunting rabbits.

——CATCHING RABBITS AND RATS. There are three methods used in ferreting—one for catching rats and two for rabbits. In rabbit hunting the ferret is muzzled with a "cope", made by looping a piece of twine around the muzzle and over the back of the ferret's head (to keep the mouth closed so that the animal cannot kill rabbits it corners in a dead-end warren). The ferret is then turned loose in the rabbit hole. The escaping rabbit is shot or netted in a bag placed over the hole.

The second practice is to hold the ferret on a line and let it down into a dead-end rabbit hole. When the hunters have determined that the ferret has come upon the rabbits, they sink holes in the ground a yard or so apart to locate the line, and trace it in this way until the rabbits are located.

Hunting for rats is a far commoner sport. Favourite places are cornfields and the vicinity of farm buildings. After finding the ratholes, the hunter unleashes his ferret without a muzzle, and then stands ready with the terriers. It is not long before the ferret drives its prey into the open. There may be a whole pack of rats—three or more—and exciting moments follow as the terriers dash after them and bring them to earth.

The male ferret is called a "hob" and the female a "jill". These animals have been dependent on man for a livelihood for so many years that they cannot survive without human care. A lost ferret will die if it is not recovered in a few days.

——HEALING POWERS OF THE FERRET. The ferret enjoys great esteem in the folklore of superstitious peasants in Europe, especially for its supposed power to heal the sick. Particularly efficacious, we are told, is milk that the ferret has instilled with a curative quality merely by tasting it. To quote an old Irishman: "Doctors give 'er up and she comin' to directly by a drop o' milk the blessed little craythur had been a-lappin' at; and it's the only rale remedy ye can put ye're intire faith in."

OTHER INTERESTING FERRETS AND POLECATS

While the Black-footed Ferret, *Mustela nigripes*, resembles the ferret and the polecat in size and general appearance, in reality it is an entirely different animal. This big, yellowish-buff weasel with the black feet is at home on the Great Plains and prairies of the United States, from North Dakota and Montana south to Texas, the region originally covered by the prairie dog towns. Since the dogs, its chief source of food, have all but disappeared on the western plains, the black-footed ferret is on the road to extinction.

In the Gobi Desert and the steppe country west to Rumania and Hungary dwells a very ornate little polecat, the Tiger Weasel, *Vormela*. The Afghans' name for it is "gorkhus" or "grave-digger", because they believe it frequents burial grounds. It is about thirteen inches long, plus a seven-inch tail, and is capable of emitting a disagreeable odour.

This animal's colour pattern is most unusual for a member of the weasel family. It is a deep reddish-brown, almost black, broken by numerous dots and dashes of reddish-brown colour.

Though a creature of the open desert, where there are a few trees, the tiger weasel climbs them freely.

MARTENS AND SABLES—PRECIOUS FUR-BEARERS

The True Martens and Sables, *Martes*, have the finest and most beautiful fur of all the carnivores—it is even more durable than that of the chinchillas. It is deep, soft, full, and generally rich golden brown in colour.

Indeed, these lords of the treetops have a most comely appearance. The head is well formed, and the ears are rather large and evenly rounded. A throat patch of creamy buff sets off the golden brown of the long body. The tail, about half the length of the cat-sized body, is bushy as a fox's.

The marten (or sable—the names are often interchanged) dwells among the thick forests of the Northern Hemisphere. An active and agile climber, it can chase up a tree like lightning. It easily outstrips the speedy squirrels, which must then pay with their lives. So many squirrels does the marten eat, that we may almost call it one of Nature's checks upon the tribe of nut hoarders.

A SAVAGE FIGHTER

Possessed of the typical ferocity of the weasel family, the marten will sometimes fight animals many times its size. There is a remarkable instance where a marten attacked a Cheviot sheep in Scotland. The sheep was found dead with its neck jammed against a rock; underneath its neck lay the marten, killed, apparently, by the impact when the sheep, in the final struggle, had dashed against the rock. The sheep had died from loss of blood through a wound in its throat.

Normally, the little marten feeds on smaller animals. Prominent on its menu are grouse, mice, and rabbits. In the autumn, when the berries are ripe on the mountain ash, the marten grows fat on this fruit.

So sharp are the marten's claws and wits, that few other creatures, other than man, can kill it. The great horned owl and the lynx are said to have occasional success. Unless its days are shortened by these animals or by trappers, the marten has a life span of seventeen years or so.

A LIFE OF COMFORT

A worshipper of warmth and comfort, the marten loves to lounge on the limb of a large tree and bask in the sunshine. Inside a hollow tree (but sometimes in a burrow) the marten builds its moss-lined den, at some distance above ground level. The animal's pet aversion is water, and on a wet day it will stay at home and go hungry rather than get its dainty feet wet. It does not hibernate in the winter.

FOUR BLIND LITTLE BABIES

The mating of martens takes place in July and August. It is a long time before the young—usually four per litter—are born. Not until April or May do they come into the world. Still, the kittens are naked, and without sight at birth. When they are five weeks old, their eyes open. Father isn't interested in the babies; their mother has complete charge until the autumn. At this time the young martens, with their long, sinuous bodies, look much like their parents and are ready to set up housekeeping on their own in the trees.

Except in the breeding season, the martens live alone and hunt alone. Squirrel-like, these animals bury excess food. Leaping from one branch to another, sometimes descending to the ground, they will hunt mile after mile, pursuing the hapless squirrels high and low, not giving up the chase until the prey has found safety in some hole too small for a marten to enter—or, more likely, has died from a sharp bite through the neck.

FATAL CURIOSITY

Although the marten has a distaste for human companionship and moves back as civilization advances, it has not learned to avoid man-made traps; in fact, it is one of the easiest animals to catch in the North Woods of Canada. The more obvious a trap, the better are its chances of catching a marten—due, no doubt, to the unrestrained curiosity of the animal.

HUNTING THE MARTEN

The high price set on the pelt of the marten—a good one is worth its weight in gold, ounce for ounce—leaves little chance of the animal's survival. It is not a fast breeder and probably mates only every second year.

Trappers have been whittling down the marten's numbers for a long time. The Hudson's Bay Company's take in 1743 was already as high as fifteen thousand pelts. Still, the animal could find comparative safety by retreating farther into more remote, snow-shrouded forests. Not so today. Using aircraft, trappers penetrate deeper and deeper into the marten's last strongholds. Some twenty thousand martens continue to be trapped annually in Canada, but according to some calculations the present stock cannot stand such a drain on its number much longer.

THE FABULOUS RUSSIAN SABLE AND OTHERS

There are a number of different species and subspecies of martens and sables. Perhaps the most famous is the Russian Sable, *Martes zibellina*, which ranges from European Russia across through Siberia to Japan. Its fur is exceedingly precious—so much so that the search for it lured men into the frozen wastes of Siberia long ago, and to no small degree laid the basis for the early development of that land, just as the hunt for the furs of other animals helped to open up Canada and the western United States.

Anyone who has ever seen Russian sable can appreciate why it is so highly valued. It is exquisitely soft, delicately textured fur; each hair is evenly tapered to a fine point. The general colour of the coat is grey-brown, with underfur varying from soft grey to light yellowish brown (though some sable pelts are almost black, beautifully and evenly flecked with white hairs). The most esteemed grade of sable skins generally comes from the smaller animals.

Artists' "Sable" Brushes. Although artists will tell you that the best brushes they use—brushes that come to a fine point when wet—are made from the hairs of the sable's tail, this is an instance of mislabelling; the so-called "sable" brushes are actually made from the hairs of the kolinsky (and that animal, we have seen, is more a weasel than a true mink).

Tassels of the Tungus. The sable is a tradition not only with those who can afford it, but also with the people in its home territory. The Tungus tribes of Siberia admire it greatly, and it plays an important part in the culture of this Mongoloid people. Elaborate decorative patterns in native clothing represent two sables fighting. The tribesmen's coats of scarlet and blue are worked in these patterns; so, too, are their gloves and shoes. Nearly every native tribesman has a tassel to his cap that is supposed to be the tail of a sable—but in most instances it turns out to be a squirrel tail!

Stone Marten and Pine Marten. The Stone Marten or Beech Marten, *Martes foina*, has fur which is not so fine as that of the more northern species. We find this animal in continental Europe and east to Mongolia and China. It is the common marten of central Eurasia but it never did occur in England. Here, the European Pine Marten, *Martes martes*, is the usual species, though it is rare today. Its range covers the wooded regions of Europe from Britain across to Asia.

The European pine marten is dark brown with a cream-buff throat patch; it has a head-and-body length of nineteen inches and a tail half as long again. Hundreds of years ago, when the creature was more abundant in England, hunting it was a favourite sport. To distinguish this animal from its evil-smelling relative the European polecat, or foumart ("foul marten"), it is sometimes called the "sweet marten".

The American Pine Marten. About the same size is the American Pine Marten, or Hudson Bay Sable, *Martes americana*, which lives chiefly in Canada from the Great Lakes north to the timber line and west to Alaska. This marten possesses a handsomer fur; it is rather pale buff-brown in colour, and shadowed with the dark tips of the long guard hairs.

The "Honey Dog". In the wooded mountainous country of eastern Asia dwells the Yellow-throated Marten, *Charronia*. It is larger than the pine marten, growing up to two feet in length, and has a longer tail (about seventeen inches). Its general body colour is dark brown, almost black; the chin and throat are white, and the under-parts are yellow or bright orange.

The Manchurians call the yellow-throated marten a *mi-kow*, or "honey dog", because it has a sweet tooth. This large, robust marten has been seen in China, now and again, sitting outside a beehive snapping at the honey bees going in and out; apparently it is attracted there by the smell of the honey.

The yellow-throated marten is also fond of fruit, berries, and nectar from flowers, and sometimes it will hang by its hind feet from one branch while reaching for fruit on another. But otherwise this animal is close to the pine marten in its ways.

THE FISHER—MOST FEROCIOUS OF THE MARTENS

The Fisher, *Martes pennanti*, is the terror of the American North Woods. When angry, it is the embodiment of unrestrained fury. Its eyes blazing with a green glow, it hisses, snarls, and screams its hatred at an aggressor. With its back arched and fur bristling, it presents a front that few animals would dare approach. It can beat any dog or coyote, or even a black bear in single combat, and send them scurrying off to lick their wounds.

The Fearless Fisher. Though streamlined like its relative the weasel, the fisher has tremendous power. Every living thing it can master (and that includes all but the largest carnivores in its home range) is food for the fisher—fox, lynx, raccoon, as well as rabbits, mice, rats, squirrels, grouse, amphibians, and reptiles are preyed on by this whirlwind spitfire. According to reports, it will kill deer, and probably mountain sheep are hard put to defend themselves against it.

Killing the Porcupine. The fisher is the only carnivorous animal that habitually assaults the porcupine and suffers no ill effects from the spines: it swallows the barbed quills like a carnival glass-chewer.

The fisher knows just how to get past the porcupine's guard without being clubbed by the needle-spiked tail. It speedily sinks its sharp teeth into the unprotected throat or the under-side, and the porcupine is no more.

For the fisher, killing the porcupine in the snow is a much-relished pastime. Sometimes the porcupine hides its vulnerable head under a rock or a log and rattles its deadly tail, daring the fisher to come closer. The wily fisher has an answer for that one; it burrows under the snow and gets the porcupine from below.

Fishers Are Big Martens. What manner of savage beast is the fisher? In reality, the animal is a large marten. It looks a good deal like the pine marten, only its fur is dark and not so fine, and the ears are shorter and more rounded. From the tip of its nose to the end of its foot-long tail it may measure four feet (females are smaller). It weighs up to eighteen pounds.

Sometimes the fisher is known as the Pekan, Pennant's Marten, or the Black "Cat". Fisher seems to be the most popular name, though oddly enough the animal does not fish.

A Great Climber, Leaper, and Swimmer. The fisher, if it is found at all, will be seen near watercourses in forested lowlands. It can swim across swift rivers and broad lakes. In the trees it is one of the swiftest of climbers, and even races down tree trunks head first (many other animals back down cautiously). Travelling on the ground, it bounds along, covering four feet at each leap.

This carnivore is a night prowler, and is active all the year round. It may stay in its den during a severe storm, but ordinary snow and rain will not keep the fisher at home.

The Fisher Family. The fisher's breeding habits remind us of the marten's. Its favourite den is a hollow tree. It mates in April, and the young are not born until eleven months later.

The fisher family consists of about four babies. They see the light of day seven weeks after birth and do not venture outside the den until they are fully three months old. Throughout, they are exclusively under their mother's care.

In the autumn, the young are ready to investigate distant fields and find a home for themselves. They reach full maturity when two years old, but females will breed within a year from birth.

A Scarce Animal. The fisher may be encountered from northern New England north-west to the lower Mackenzie River, Canada, south in the Rocky Mountains to Wyoming, and almost to San Francisco Bay on the Pacific coast. Though it has lingered longer than the marten in many parts of its range—a clever beast, it readily recognizes traps and is adept at robbing them—it never was very common anywhere, and is now quite rare, even in remote parts of Canada.

Today there is on an average not more than one fisher to a hundred square miles in its present range. Most of the pelts that come into the market are from Quebec, Ontario, and British Columbia.

TAYRAS, GRISONS, AND ZORILLAS

"WEASEL BADGERS" OF SOUTH AMERICA

South America has its own particular group of "weasel badgers". Largest of all is the Tayra, *Eira*, which haunts the tropical forests and brush country from southern Mexico to Bolivia and Paraguay. The tayra measures two feet in length without the seventeen-inch tail, and is a long-bodied, short-legged animal, coal-black in colour except for the head and neck, which vary from almost black to nearly white.

Being a good climber, the tayra spends much of its time in the trees hunting for fruit, berries, and birds' eggs, but almost anything edible is food for it. It is socially inclined and travels in family groups. This animal's bold and curious nature is often its undoing; it will fearlessly approach an armed man and learn too late he is no one to take lightly.

A much smaller animal, the Grison, *Grison*, is a neighbour of the tayra. It resembles a tiny grey badger and lives in the ground. We can distinguish it from yet another interesting "weasel badger", the Quiqui or Huron, *Grisonella*, of Argentina and Chile, but the broad white line that extends across the face and back along the outside of the grison's neck. The quiqui is trained by the natives to drive the chinchillas out of their dens in the rocks.

ZORILLAS AND STRIPED "WEASELS"

On the other side of the world there are a number of other small carnivores that also combine characteristics of both the weasels and badgers. The Zorilla, *Ictonyx*, known locally as the Striped Muishond ("mouse hound"), is the most familiar species in Africa. It ranges from the Cape north to the Isthmus of Suez and into Asia Minor. Its long, loose fur is marked with black and white lines that extend from the head to the lengthy white tail. This creature is not more than fifteen inches in head-and-body length.

In general the zorilla and its close relatives (among them there is a Striped "Weasel") are useful animals as they destroy large numbers of snakes, small rodents, and injurious insects (they will also kill birds up to the size of a guinea fowl). When attacked by dogs, the zorilla ejects a nauseating musky fluid in the face of the attacker and then feigns death until the coast is clear. Thus it combines in its defence the pacifist characteristic of the American opossum with the positive action of the skunk.

WOLVERINES—RUTHLESS DESTROYERS

The Wolverine, *Gulo*, is one of the most thievish, daring, and powerful animals in the world. It is the biggest member of the weasel family, and none exceeds it in ferocity and cunning.

NOT MUCH LIKE A WOLF

The wolverine got its name because it was supposed to resemble the wolf. It possesses that animal's savage nature, but in general it is built more like a badger. The fearless wolverine will slay almost any animal in its range, including the deer.

Not many people know this shaggy, four-foot-long creature that prowls the northlands. But as it stalks along, the animals that glimpse the dark-brown bearlike form, with the telltale broad ribbon of pale brown fur on each side, start up and look for refuge. Even the massive bear, the wolf, and the mountain lion, gorging themselves on their kill, will move off rather than contest its possession against the sharp claws and teeth of the wolverine.

NO QUARTER ASKED OR GIVEN

The wolverine is a killer. When it fights, it fights to win; it neither asks nor gives quarter, and it does not know the meaning of fear.

Not fast on foot when compared to the caribou and mountain sheep, the wolverine captures both of these large animals by stalking them stealthily and craftily. It will climb into a tree or up on a high rock and leap upon them, sinking its teeth into their neck. Almost no four-footed animal, including the bear and possibly the puma, is secure against its attack.

Trappers hate the wolverine. Their traps, to it, are like so many free-lunch counters. It will remove the bait and eat it, then, more likely than not, damage the traps or carry them off.

Woe betide the trapper whose cabin the wolverine enters! Later he will find everything in confusion: tea, flour, pots, and pans are scattered hither and yon, his meat supply is gone, and the foul odour of the animal's scent glands is everywhere. What the wolverine cannot eat, it befouls. This is the way it protects its own caches, too, from other prowlers.

"THE GLUTTON"

The wolverine got its name because of its supposed resemblance to the wolf, either in its looks or its habits or both. It is also known as the Carcajou or Skunk-Bear. Another common name, and well deserved at that, is "glutton". This animal indeed possesses a ravenous appetite. It appears always to be hungry. No other carnivore, we are sometimes told, can devour so much in a single meal.

Occasionally the wolverine will clean up a whole deer or a caribou in what may seem to be a continuous feast, but what is really a number of successive meals. Accordingly, there is a tradition that the wolverine consumes more than its own weight in food at one time. This is simply not true. An average wolverine weighs thirty or thirty-five pounds; a big one, fifty. It never eats such a poundage in one repast. To understand this ferocious beast's hunger, you must realize that there are long gaps between its meals; sometimes its fasts may last a week or two.

The famous old scientists Linnaeus and Pallas showed they were well acquainted with the wolverine's habits when they named one common species *Gulo luscus*. The first half of the name means "glutton"; the second half refers to the animal's poor eyesight, and could be translated as "half-blind". The wolverine gives marked evidence that it cannot see well. It will sit up on its haunches and shade its eyes with a fore paw in a most human manner. This curious habit has been witnessed on several occasions, and one of the animals frequently repeated the performance. Since the wolverine is subject to snow-blindness, we may suppose it shields its eyes to protect them from bright sunlight when peering into the distance.

THE SOLITARY WOLVERINE

The wolverine is solitary in its habits. After a brief courtship in February or early March, the male and female split up, each going its own way.

The female's den may be a hollow tree, a cavern among rocks, or any hideaway that is comfortable and sheltered. Here, during the warm days of June, when the sun never sets in the northland for four long weeks, the young—they rarely number more than two or three —are born. The babies are clad in thick woolly fur. Their mother takes good care of them, and by autumn they are half grown. When the first snow flies, they must forage for themselves.

A FUR THAT DOES NOT FREEZE

Wolverine fur is not outstandingly valuable in the fur market, but it does have a unique use. It is the only type of fur that does not mat and freeze when the temperature drops to sixty or seventy degrees below zero. The Eskimos are well aware of this: they trim their parkas with wolverine fur around the hood and sleeves, where body moisture escapes. Any ordinary fur will freeze to the face and wrists under conditions of extreme cold, but wolverine fur remains unchanged. Nowadays the makers of airmen's clothing are borrowing a leaf from the Eskimos' book.

The range of the wolverine in North America extends from the southern islands of the Arctic Ocean across the Barren Lands to southern Quebec in the east, and to Colorado and south-eastern California in the west. It is now practically gone from the United States; the last individual had disappeared from Michigan, the Wolverine State, long before any official record was made that the species had been exterminated there.

There are three species found in North America: the American Wolverine, the Mt. McKinley Wolverine, and the Southern Wolverine. In Europe and Asia, the animal is found in the Arctic and sub-Arctic regions, but it is fast vanishing everywhere.

BADGERS—FAMED AS DIGGERS

THE COMMON BADGER OF EUROPE AND ASIA

The Eurasian Badger, *Meles*, was the subject of a bloody sport in England in the early part of the last century. This tough, wedge-shaped little animal was placed in a barrel or a man-made hole inside a pit, and dogs were loosed upon it. With its long, sharp claws and its strong teeth, it fought back as best it could as the dogs tried to draw it from its hole.

This cruel pastime, ended by law in 1850, has left its mark in our language, but nowadays we are more likely to badger people than to badger the badger.

The Badger's Badge. Upon its face the Eurasian badger wears the badge for which it is named. Each side of the white head is marked with a conspicuous black line that runs from the nose over and surrounding the eye and over the ear. Its body looks grey to us, for each hair is partly black and partly white. (Badger hair is used in the manufacture of the best shaving brushes; in fact, the French word *blaireau* means both "shaving brush" and "badger".)

This animal measures up to three feet long, and, with its short black legs and stump of a tail, suggests a small bear. It weighs about twenty-seven pounds, on an average.

The Badger at Home. Lacking the ferocity of the weasel and the wolverine, the badger prefers to use its claws for digging. A shy, cautious creature, it spends the daylight hours underground, in the home it has excavated for itself. Its den, or "earth", is usually in a wooded hillside, at the end of "sets", or holes, which may penetrate for a hundred yards or more. These subterranean tunnels form a winding labyrinth three (badger) stories deep. The entrances are always marked by huge piles of dirt, indicating that the animal is constantly at work enlarging and improving the "earth".

The badger likes to sleep on a bed of dry leaves, moss, and straw. But first it must collect them and bring them underground, and it goes about the job in a most painstaking way. To begin with, the badger gathers the bedding up into a small heap. Next it cuddles the bundle between its forepaws and nose. Taking care that it does not lose any of its cargo, the badger shuffles backward to the entrance. Now it backs down into the hole, and so to the den.

Mating Time. It is not unusual for several families to occupy the same badger "earth" during August and September, but they separate before the winter sets in. Mating season for the badgers extends from July to mid-November. The sow normally has one litter a year, in February or March. Her usual number of babies is two, but occasionally she bears triplets. The young grow rapidly, and are ready to leave the care of their parents in the autumn.

Badgers never depart from their dens before dark. Then they hunt for all manner of animals, including beetles, worms, hedgehogs, small rodents, and rabbits. They readily detect their prey by scent and dig them out of the ground if necessary. Fruits, nuts, and vegetables are also food for the badger, which may store them in its den in the autumn, for winter use. It does not hibernate, but may sleep when the temperature drops to or below zero.

A Remarkable Badger "Funeral". The badgers have few natural enemies, and many live out the normal life span of ten years. They probably die in an underground chamber, which is then sealed off by other tenants of the badger "earth". There is even on record one remarkable instance of a badger "funeral". The event—it took place in England—was witnessed by Brian Vesey-Fitzgerald in 1941.

A female badger was seen excavating a large hole in an abandoned rabbit warren. Her efforts were interrupted by several journeys which she made back and forth between the rabbit warren and her set. All the time she seemed agitated and uttered strange and perhaps mournful cries.

The excavation completed, the female was joined by another badger, a male, and both retreated to the set. A short time later he was seen dragging a dead badger by the leg (another male—it could have been her mate) with the female giving some assistance from the rear. The body was duly deposited in the open grave and covered with earth. The female returned home; the helpful male went elsewhere and was not seen again.

Where We Find Them. The range of the Old World badgers reaches from the British Isles and Spain across Europe and northern Asia to Japan; the southern limit in Asia is the Himalayas. The badgers of Eurasia are separable into four general groups: the typical or European Badger, the Siberian Badger, the Caucasian Badger, and the Japanese Badger.

THE AMERICAN BADGER

The American Badger, *Taxidea*, is a superb digger, like its Old World kinsman. Using all four feet, it can sink underground in a matter of a few seconds. It is perhaps the fastest excavator in America; according to reports, it can outdig both the pocket gopher and the mole, famous masters of the trade.

The badger makes the most of its long, powerful claws. It feeds to a large extent on ground squirrels, which it digs out of their burrows. By some ingenious method of calculation, known only to itself, the badger sinks a shaft straight down to the spot where the rodent is concealed. It rarely, if ever, misses the exact location, and so saves itself the almost impossible job of trying to catch its prey by entering and widening the squirrels' long tunnel from the entrance. When the victims are more than the badger has an appetite for, it will bury their carcasses against a leaner day.

Lizards, insects, gophers, rabbits, mice, and birds—these, also, the badger pursues. When larger animals pursue it in turn, it will fight back—unless they are just too large, like the coyote. Then the badger seeks safety underground.

We find the American badger in central North America from the Great Lakes region north through Alberta and British Columbia, and south-west through Nebraska to California and northern Mexico. (Wisconsin is known as the Badger State, but not simply because of its badgers. The allusion is to the early lead miners, who dug their winter homes in its hillsides, we are told.)

The American badger is a creature of the open country, often making its home in plains, prairies, and deserts. Here it lives four or five feet below the surface in a cosy den which it lines with dry leaves or grass, like its Eurasian relatives. It reaches the den by means of a tunnel many feet in length. During the day, it remains indoors.

MORE ACTIVE THAN IT LOOKS

The American badger is a squat, heavy-bodied animal with large claws, at home on the plains and in the forests of North America. It encounters few animals big enough to be a menace to it; if it feels itself endangered, it can quickly dig its way to safety in the ground. The badger is not a swift runner, and it is not able to climb up a tree.

The Badger in Winter. In the northern limits of its range the badger puts on fat during the autumn and then holes up for the winter, blocking the tunnel to its den with soil. It does not go into a true state of hibernation, but alternately drowses and wakens. Occasionally it will leave its den and go hunting across the snow, but it eats little during the food-scarce cold months. In the south it remains active all the year round.

"Delayed" Babies. The American badger mates in the late autumn of the year or in the early winter. Apparently the development of the babies in the mother's body is delayed for the first two months in regions where it is really cold (this does not happen with the Eurasian badger) and the total period may take thirteen weeks.

Two to seven blind and hairless young are born as late as May or June in northern areas. They open their eyes when they are about five weeks old; now they are half grown and ready to be weaned. From this time until they are two-thirds grown, the mother brings food to them or (later) takes them on hunting trips.

By autumn the young badgers are big fellows, and move off in different directions, each to claim a domain of its own, as their mother enters a new breeding season.

Coarse Fur, but Useful. Much like their relatives in Europe and Asia, the American badgers are flattened, stocky, short-legged animals, with very short tails. They stand about nine inches at the shoulder, are two feet long or more, and weigh from twelve to twenty-four pounds, being somewhat smaller than the Eurasian badger.

The animal's general colour is silvery grey. The face is dark brown and marked with a narrow central white stripe; the cheeks are white, too. The "badge" is thus quite different from the Eurasian badger's.

American badger fur is rather coarse and is used for coat trimming; it is much too soft to be satisfactory for shaving brushes. There is only one species of American badger, with three varying regional types.

The American Badger on Trial. The badger is often considered a pest. People know the animal is a digger; when they ride along on horseback and are thrown because the horse has put its foot in a hole, they blame the badger. So the poor creature frequently gets shot on sight.

The evidence against the badger is, as it happens, of a highly circumstantial nature, and would not stand up in a court of wild-life experts. They would rather point out that there are plenty of other diggers on the prairies; why blame the badger alone? The animal kills venomous snakes and every year destroys a large number of rodents that are troublesome to crops. For the great good it does, the badger well deserves commutation of the all-too-frequent death sentence.

It should be said, too, in favour of the American badgers, that like their Old World counterparts they can be tamed if taken young.

As a group martens, or sables, have the finest fur of all the carnivores but the quality varies with different species. A "sun worshipper", the marten dislikes water so much that on a rainy day it will stay at home and go hungry rather than get its feet wet.   *See page 508*

[5-3]

Largest member of the weasel family, the wolverine is one of the most thievish, daring, powerful animals in the world. A ruthless killer, the wolverine makes sport of trappers, not only eating their bait but usually carrying off or destroying the traps as well   *See page 515*

[5-3A]

[5-4]

[5-4A]

The American badger is one of the fastest excavators in the Western Hemisphere. Feeding mainly on ground squirrels, it will sink a shaft straight down to the spot where its prey is concealed, seldom if ever missing the exact spot. *See page 520*

The two musk glands of the skunk can be discharged separately or simultaneously, projecting a fine spray of their infamous evil-smelling fluid a distance of nine feet or more. Apparently even the skunk finds the odour objectionable— it is always very careful not to defile itself. *See page 524*

[5-5]

With its streamlined body and large webbed hind feet, the North American otter is the speedster of the fresh water lakes and rivers. Companionable and gentle with its associates, this member of the weasel family is above even the suspicion of having bad habits. Its favourite pastime is coasting down steep mud- or snowbanks.

See page 530

The sea otter rarely comes to land. It loves to float, and on its back will idly propel itself with its tail. In a hurry, it flips over and races through the water at ten miles per hour. The big otter brings up shellfish and crustaceans from depths of 100 feet or more and, with the catch laid out on its chest and belly, enjoys a leisurely lunch.   *See page 531*

[5-5A]

The genet is a member of the large family of "weasel cats" so called simply because they combine characteristics of both animals. They have one great advantage over their related carnivores — when the meat supply dwindles, they eat insects, fruit and vegetables whereas the strictly flesh eating weasels and cats are faced with starvation.

People who have reared them declare they make friendly, intelligent pets.

BADGERS OF FAR-OFF LANDS

Badgers with Warning Signals. There are other badgers, but about them we hear little for they live in remote parts of the earth. The Sand or Hog Badger, *Arctonyx*, of south-eastern Asia, has a white tail that is comparatively long for a badger; while on the islands of Java, Sumatra, and Borneo dwells the Teledu, *Mydaus*, a small brown badger with a broad white band down its back. These white markings are the warning signals often carried by animals capable of discouraging possible enemies by discharging an offensive-smelling liquid musk.

The Ratel. Throughout Africa and in Asia Minor and southern Asia the Ratel, *Mellivora*, is as famous as the badger is in Europe and the New World. Enjoying the reputation of a fearless and desperate fighter, it is a powerful, thickset animal about the size of a badger, with tiny ears.

In colour the ratel's fur coat is usually grey or white on the back and jet black below; as you might suppose from its skunklike colour scheme, it is protected from many of its enemies by its fetid discharge.

The ratel is at home in the rocky hills, on the grassy plains, and in the forests (though it does not climb trees). Armed with powerful claws, it can tear down termite nests and ant-hills to get at the larvae; reptiles, rodents, rabbits, and birds, as well as fruit, are also included in its diet.

The ratel's thick hide, which covers its body like a loose coat of rubber, is impervious alike to the fangs of venomous snakes, the quills of porcupines, and the stings of bees. The animal is partial to honey in particular, and forms an interesting association with the little bird known as the Honey-Guide. On discovering a bees' nest, this bird emits a series of high-pitched notes that are recognized by the ratel. Following the cries of the bird, the animal soon discovers the bees' nest and proceeds to tear it apart, gorging itself on the young bees and honey. The bird, too, comes in for a share of the feast, which it could not have without the aid of the ratel.

Its hunger satisfied, the ratel lies up in a den among the rocks or in a hole in the ground. It is not a social creature and travels either singly or in pairs. The female gives birth to a litter of only two cubs six months after mating, which explains why the ratel is never very

IT KNOWS HOW TO DEFEND ITSELF

The ratel is to Africa and parts of Asia what the badger is to Europe and America. This lively animal is a prodigious digger, and can also climb trees when it has to. Its strong claws and teeth will make almost any enemy think twice before attacking it. When disturbed, the ratel produces a powerful stench like the skunk.

common anywhere. It has a rather long life expectancy for a member of the weasel family: the ratel has been known to live over twenty-three years in captivity.

SKUNKS—DANGEROUS BUT NOT DEADLY

The Common or Striped Skunk, *Mephitis*, and its equally unpopular relatives, the Hog-nosed Skunk and the Little Spotted Skunk, are American animals famous for the degree to which they have perfected the art of defensive chemical warfare.

Some Old World members of the weasel family, we have seen, can make themselves objectionable by ejecting a foul-smelling fluid, but the discharge they fire is mild and ineffective compared with the barrage set off by the "big guns" of the skunks. (Most weasels and badgers cannot actually spray their odour, and we suspect that in many of these animals it is used primarily in the mating season.)

Not so with the skunk. Provoke it, and you will learn to your sorrow that it can project a fine spray for a distance of nine feet or more. The fluid has a most distasteful and nauseating stench and produces intense smarting and burning if it comes in contact with the membranes of the eyes, nose or mouth. If it penetrates clothing, the odour may not depart for weeks.

THE SKUNK'S BIG GUNS IN ACTION

The skunk always carries two "guns" primed and ready to fire. They are really two large musk glands situated at the base of the tail. When the skunk becomes frightened or annoyed, it contracts the muscles surrounding the glands, forcing out the spray. With a good wind blowing, the smell may carry farther than half a mile.

The skunk can discharge one "gun" or fire both simultaneously. The first barrage is the most powerful, but there is enough ammunition for six successive "shots". After the "magazine" is empty, it is a little while before it is reloaded.

Not an animal that wastes its ammunition, the skunk uses it generally as a last resort only. Confronted with a formidable foe, the little stench-bearer first growls its displeasure and stamps its foot impatiently. If this is ineffective, its white striped tail, bristling with tension, is raised as a final warning, but fire is withheld so long as the very tip of the tail hangs limp. One step nearer by the intruder—up goes the tip of the tail—and the broadside is discharged with deadly accuracy at the head of the foe.

A direct hit at close range will cause tears to flow freely and produce temporary blindness. While the victim howls in pain, the skunk ambles off, as fragrant and pure as ever, for it is always careful not to defile itself with the evil-smelling liquid.

It is an odd and interesting fact that the malodorous oily yellow fluid produced by the skunk can be put to a pleasing use by man. He extracts it from the animal and refines it, removing the disagreeable smell. The liquid that remains has a great capacity to fix and retain aromas. Have you guessed yet the end that awaits the skunk's secretion? It is blended with subtle and alluring scents, and the result is—fine perfume!

ANOTHER ANIMAL WITH A STINK-SCREEN

The common or striped skunk bears white stripes of warning on its back. If an animal disregards this danger signal and attempts to molest the skunk, it can discharge a foul-smelling liquid, surrounding itself with an almost impenetrable stink-screen. Sometimes man extracts the fluid and uses it to produce fine perfume. "Deskunked", this creature makes a docile and pleasing pet.

EASY-GOING WAYS OF THE SKUNK

Perfectly aware of its power of defence, the skunk is slow and deliberate in its actions. If unmolested, it strolls along good-naturedly. Now and then it will stop to dig up a nest of yellowjackets (wasps) with its sharp claws, and eat the grubs, for insects are a staple in its diet. Or it may speed up to a trot and catch a fleeing mouse, snake, or frog. All kinds of creeping things are food for the skunk, as well as berries, fruits, and grain. People seldom see this hungry little carnivore on its foraging trips, however, for it is active mostly at night.

By day the skunk rests or sleeps. Its den is a hollow log or, more often, a burrow in the ground. During the very cold days in the winter the skunk stays at home; at this time it lives off the layers of fat it acquired in the autumn, but it does not hibernate.

MATING AND MOTHERHOOD

Even before the winter snows start to melt, the male skunks travel far and wide to pay their respects to the females, which remain comfortably at home. Two suitors may fight bitterly for the possession of a female; they may even forget the "laws of decency" and defile each other with their obnoxious sprays. The mating season lasts through February and March.

Some fifty days after mating time the young are born—there are four to eight of them, without sight or furry coats. The mother can nurse six babies at once; if there are more, they must wait their turn. The babies open their eyes when three weeks old, and fourteen days later they are out following their mother in single file. At the age of two months they are weaned, and depend on their own resources in early autumn.

AN IDEAL PET

A young skunk is easy to capture and soon learns to be tame. The scent glands can be removed and thereafter the animal generally is an ideal pet, docile and loving. It will, incidentally, keep a house free of rodents.

SKUNK OR "ALASKA SABLE"?

The striped skunk is at home in Canada, the United States, and as far south as Honduras. About the size of a house cat, it stands seven inches at the shoulder, and is roughly eighteen inches long, plus a seven-inch tail.

Fully grown, the animal may weigh from four to ten pounds. On the glossy coat of long, limp hair, two broad white lines (united on the head) run backward down the sides of the body to the tip of the bushy tail. The face has a single stripe from the forehead to the middle of the nose. However, the amount of white varies with the animal, some skunks being almost completely black, and a fair number of subspecies have been named.

Skunks are not very wary when it comes to traps, and great numbers of these creatures are taken each year. Their pelts are in demand in the fur trade, which frequently sells them under the more pleasing names of "Alaska sable" or "black marten".

SPOTTED AND HOG-NOSED SKUNKS

Considerably smaller than the striped skunk is the Spotted Skunk, *Spilogale*, a slender, weasel-like animal that weighs only one or two pounds. Its body colour is about equally divided between black and white, the white markings being a series of more or less broken narrow lines that give us the impression of spots. Only from ten to fourteen inches in head-and-body length, this little creature has a tail about five or six inches long, and quite bushy.

SMALLER THAN A HOUSE CAT

The little spotted skunk is an expert in chemical warfare, just like its big cousin the striped skunk. Few animals will venture to bother it as it roams about in search of the small insects it generally feeds on. A lynx or a great horned owl will, however, occasionally make a meal of this relative of the weasel.

The spotted skunk has a habit of standing on its front paws and holding the rear end of its body in the air like a schoolboy showing off. This is often done in play, but it is also a warning signal. The little spotted skunk is so small that it has to raise its body up to get a good "shot" at a dog or a fox.

"Phoby Cat". Sometimes called the "polecat" or "little striped skunk", in the southern states this small creature is also known as the "phoby cat", or "hydrophobia cat". During the mating season the extraordinary actions of the little spotted skunk seem to border on insanity.

It is reported that in its mating madness the spotted skunk has entered a wolf's den, taken the cubs by the ears, and shaken and knocked them about generally; also it is said to have sprayed a bull full in the face.

But there is no scientific reason for thinking this small stench-bearer is more subject to hydrophobia than any other animal, and in other respects its habits are much the same as those of other members of the skunk tribe.

The little spotted skunk makes its home from southern British Columbia in the west and northern Virginia in the east through Mexico to Costa Rica. It is a creature of the plains and the dry desert regions. Its long, soft fur is known as "civet cat" in the fur trade. Civet cats, as such, are entirely different animals, of course, and are discussed in a later chapter.

A Nose for Insects. In the south-western United States we come upon a much larger species, the Hog-nosed Skunk, *Conepatus*, that also makes its home through Mexico and as far south as Chile and Patagonia. A robust animal about the size of a striped skunk, it possesses a striking adaptation for getting its livelihood: the head is long and the muzzle naked, somewhat like a hog's snout. With this remarkable natural tool, the hog-nosed skunk roots in the ground for insects, which make up a good part of its diet.

Rather coarse black or brownish-black fur clothes this skunk, and, along its back, from the top of the head to the tip of the tail, there runs a broad white band, but this is variable—there may be two white lines or very little white indeed, particularly in the South American skunks.

We have already observed that poisonous animals or bad-tasting ones seem to advertise their nature to creatures that might otherwise make the mistake of attacking them. In the case of the skunks, the striking white marking, standing out against the black, provides an effective warning and—by no means incidentally—protects the bearers.

OTTERS—PLAYFUL FISHERMEN

THE NORTH AMERICAN OTTER

The North American Otter, *Lutra canadensis*, is the fastest mammal in the freshwater lakes and rivers of its homeland. There it cruises along at six miles per hour, but it can go much faster if need be. It can swim a quarter of a mile under water, remaining submerged four minutes and more without coming up for air.

Above all else, otters are fishermen. They have been known to kill a fish up to twenty pounds in weight; usually, however, the quarry is much smaller. At times they take the cunning trout, but they are more inclined to hunt easier prey such as sunfish and other sluggish varieties. The otters catch the fish with their forepaws, then rip it apart with their teeth.

Except during the breeding season, otters are continually on the move and will travel a twenty-mile circuit of connecting lakes and rivers in two or three weeks. Where there is good fishing, they remain awhile, but not for long. When the water freezes over, they often travel overland, looking for rivers or rapids that are still flowing. Unlucky are the ducks, muskrats, and young beavers the otters encounter, for these fishermen like to vary their diet now and then. They are active both day and night.

The otter is streamlined for darting through water. It has a lithe, muscular body, a broad, flat head, small ears, and a long, powerful, tapering tail which serves as a rudder. Its limbs are short, but the strong hind feet are large and broadly webbed. Its oily coat is a rich dark brown in colour, with very full and dense fur that keeps the animal warm in the water.

Few animals will attack this water-loving member of the weasel family. When a large beast goes after it, the otter escapes by diving into the water or, in winter, alternately racing and sliding across the snow. Sometimes it will stand and fight. It can give a good account of itself, even against dogs.

Favourite Otter Games. In character the otter is above even the suspicion of having bad habits. It is gentle and friendly with all its associates, and likes to sport and play.

This animal's favourite pastime is to coast down a steep "slide" as children love to do; in the summer the bank of a stream is used.

Taking turns, a family of otters will plunge down one after the other in quick succession, the water from their bodies greasing the slide and heightening the fun. In winter the highest snowbank in the vicinity is used for a slide, and the sport becomes fast and hilarious until danger threatens or play has to be abandoned in favour of food.

The Otters at Home. The otter's den is usually a hole in the bank of a stream or lake. This swimmer likes quick and easy access to its home, and so the main entrance is under water. There is a back door, too, used for ventilation, and this, for safety's sake, is hidden in the bushes on the bank. For comfort, soft moss and dry leaves line the floor of the den.

We are not sure exactly when the otter's mating season occurs, and there is some question as to whether or not both parents take part in raising the family. The baby otters are born in April or May and as a rule they are twins; occasionally there are three, but rarely more. It is a month before their eyes open; then the young are taught to swim.

For the first few trips in the water, the young otters ride on the mother's back. One day she submerges and leaves the kittens to struggle as best they can in the shallow water. Now it is sink or swim—well, not exactly so, for Mother is always close by to help if serious difficulties should arise.

Otters raised in captivity are esteemed as pets, and some do eminent service as retrievers, particularly of waterfowl. With a normal life span of eight or nine years, otters may live up to the age of sixteen under favourable conditions.

There is little variation in the general appearance and habits of the otter throughout its entire range. This valuable fur-bearer and its related species cover most of North America, though they are not so abundant as in former times. They may be found within a fifty-mile radius of some of the largest cities of North America. On an average, they weigh about twenty pounds and are some thirty inches in length, plus the foot-long tail.

SEA OTTERS—BIGGEST OF THEIR TRIBE

The Sea Otter, *Enhydra*, is as much at home in the sea as a seal. The greatest of the otters, it was friendly and trusting when first discovered, but persistent, relentless hunting for its valuable fur has made it extremely shy of man, and whittled down its numbers. Today it rarely comes to land. Instead, it passes its life offshore in great beds of floating kelp, a type of brown seaweed. Its range is limited to the shores of the North Pacific.

"Saltiest" of the Otters. The otters of our inland waterways, adept as they are in lakes and rivers, rate as mere landlubbers beside the salty sea otter. It is born in the water, it eats in the water, sleeps in the water, grows old and dies in the water.

The sea otter loves to float, and swims as easily as a fish. Generally it lies on its back and propels itself with its tail. For greater speed it turns right side up, and, its body undulating, it strikes out with both webbed hind feet. Sometimes it uses them in unison, sometimes alternately. Often it races along at a rate of ten miles per hour.

Though the sea otter takes some fish, it is not a confirmed fisherman. It may go down a hundred feet or more in search of its daily fare, dredging from the ocean floor sea urchins, crustaceans, cuttlefish, mussels, clams, abalone, and other shellfish. Bringing its victims back to the surface, the sea otter spreads the lunch out on its belly and chest, and leisurely eats as it floats on its back.

Like most mammals that live in the water, this one does not drink, though it consumes some salt water with its food.

Scratching Itself in the Water. You might suppose the sea otter would find it a problem to scratch itself in the water. Nothing could be farther from the truth. Not only does the sea otter find scratching with one, or two, or three paws easy—this water-dweller can scratch with all four at once, each paw working in a different spot and in a different direction.

Life of a Baby Sea Otter. Sea otters are scarce, and we lack complete knowledge of their life history. We believe, however, that they breed throughout the year and that the parents mate for life. Nine months after mating time a single pup is born—not in a nest or den but on a thick bed of floating kelp. The locale usually is a sheltered natural harbour. Sometimes, though, it is a rocky island, but one that is bare of human habitation and a safe distance offshore. Unlike so many of the weasel's cousins, the pup is born with its eyes wide open.

Nursing her baby, watching over it, and giving it good care take up a large part of the mother sea otter's time for six months or even a year. Doing all of these things in the water is an art. The mother suckles her pup as she floats on her back in the water. (Sea otters normally spend their resting and sleeping hours floating in this fashion among beds of kelp.) In a playful mood, often she tosses it in the air and catches it again.

Travelling with baby, Mrs. Sea Otter lies on her back in the water and paddles along with her webbed hind feet, clutching the pup to her breast with her tiny but strong front paws. When she must go off for food, she leaves her little one floating hidden in the kelp.

Mrs. Sea Otter does not approve of dirty children. She often gives her pup a very thorough cleaning, and none too gently at that. She rolls the baby first one way and then another, carefully cleaning its fur with her teeth and tongue from end to end. When this ordeal is over, the pup relaxes on her chest and goes to sleep with its little feet folded across its belly, its paws clasped over its chest.

A sea otter mother's love for her young one is such that she will expose herself to death rather than desert the baby. If it is taken from her, she will cry bitterly like a small child. (So, too, will the baby.) Even when a pup is a year old, and a new baby is born, the family will stay together—perhaps much longer, so strong are the bonds of affection. At four years of age, the pups are fully grown.

We have said that the sea otter is the largest of the otters. What little it may lose in length when compared with one of its big relatives, the giant river otter of Brazil, it more than gains in bulk. A big sea otter may weigh up to eighty pounds; its head-and-body length varies from three to four feet, and the tail adds another foot. A heavy, thickset animal, it is much less sleek and graceful in appearance than the river otters. The pelt is very full, soft, and deep; it is brownish black in colour and more or less finely grizzled.

The Sea Otter's Fight for Survival. With the exception of the lurking killer whale, the sea otter has few natural enemies. Even at its slow rate of reproduction it maintained a fair population before its fur became commercially valuable. But when a sea otter pelt brought one hundred to twenty-five hundred dollars, overhunting became the rule, and the species was well-nigh exterminated.

Fortunately, conservationists took an interest in the matter: today the sea otter enjoys full protection in accordance with an international code that provides refuge and outlaws the sale of pelts. Over a period of years strict enforcement of this code has saved the animal from being wiped out altogether. In time we may glimpse the fascinating sea otter more and more, playing and hunting in its favourite haunts off the shores of the Pacific, from southern California to the Kurile Islands.

OTHER INTERESTING OTTERS

Otters are much alike, wherever we find them. The South and Central American otters differ from the North American species only in size and certain minor features. Perhaps the most noteworthy is the Giant Otter, Saro, or Flat-tailed Otter of Brazil, *Pteronura*. A native of the waters of the Amazon River basin, it is one of the largest river otters, measuring five feet in length.

In Australia, Madagascar, and on the islands of the South Pacific we do not encounter the otters, but they are common throughout the Old World. Some have marked peculiarities. In the Clawless Otter, *Paraonyx*, an African animal, the forefeet are small, with five naked fingers without claws; only the third and fourth fingers on the hind feet bear minute claws. Its big cousin, the Giant African Otter, *Aonyx*, weighs sixty pounds and may be longer than five feet. Dark brown in colour, it is often tinted with white and has a broad splash of white on its throat and chin. This otter's claws, too, are rudimentary or absent altogether, so that it lacks adequate defences against its dreaded enemy the crocodile.

In Asia and Sumatra we even find a Hairy-nosed Otter, *Lutra sumatrana;* the nose pad, naked in most species, is covered with fine hair, but whether this has any special use as an adaptation cannot be said.

The Eurasian Otter, *Lutra lutra*, dwells in the rivers throughout the Old World from England west to Burma and southern China, and from the Mediterranean region of Africa north to the Arctic coast. It is hunted with otter hounds in England and France, a sport that dates back to the Middle Ages, when it was the pastime of royalty.

Otters, we have observed, are sociable creatures on land. It is believed that, in the water, they often act in concert and surround or drive a shoal of fish. One reputable observer in India saw six otters swim out in a semicircle on Chilka Lake, each about fifty yards from the next. Every now and then one otter would dive and retrieve a fish, carry it to the bank, and hurry back to join the ranks of its fellow fishermen.

Genets, Civets, Mongooses, and their Kin—Lithe "Weasel Cats"

COMBINE the long, slender body of the weasel—a rough representation of the head of the fox—the short limbs of the marten —and the tail and disposition of the cat—and there you have the "weasel cats", as we may call this group. In the warmer parts of the Old World they have taken the place occupied by the weasels in the north.

Many of the weasel cats have scent glands, like the weasel family. Some of these creatures—in this they resemble the members of the cat family—possess sharp claws, which they carry sheathed in their feet when there is no need to slash or climb. (Others have nail-like claws that cannot be moved in and out.) Again like their cousins the cats, the genets, civets, and mongooses walk softly and spring swiftly upon their prey.

There is a large army of weasel cats, and they control the many small animals that breed at high speed the year round in tropical regions. Beasts of prey, they are nevertheless ready to compromise with hard times. When rodents and small game abound, these resourceful little carnivores live by killing. However, a dearth of animal life is no major catastrophe for them, as it would be for the cats or the weasels proper; the weasel cats supplement their flesh diet with insects, fruit, and even vegetables.

The weasel cats are not considered high-class fur-bearers, though the pelts of some species are used. Often the coats they wear are quite handsome. The fur of many is ornately or even gaily marked with spots and stripes, while a good number of these creatures are brightly coloured. All make up a family called the Viverridae, a name which comes from the Latin word for "ferret".

GENETS—SMALL, SAVAGE MARAUDERS

Today no one but the specialist seems to consider the genets either exciting or a promising subject for study—yet these beautiful, graceful creatures never fail to attract the attention of the person who sees them. The European genet's soft, greyish fur is dappled with black. It was popular in the past and was sold in European markets as far back as A.D. 600, but has long since fallen into disrepute.

The genet is not a large animal; the many species range between eighteen and twenty-three inches in head-and-body length; the tapering tail, about as long again, is ornately banded with dark brown or black rings.

The pointed face, with prominent ears, sits gracefully on a long, slender body with short legs. The animal's sharp hooked claws may be drawn in or extended, like a cat's; they are not only well suited for climbing trees but also for striking down fast-moving prey. Running down the genet's back there is a line of stiff hairs which stand erect when the beast is excited.

The genet, in its various forms, has an enormous range: it is found all the way from Spain in southern Europe to western Asia, and south through East Africa to the Cape. (It is commonest in Africa.) For some strange reason, the creature has bypassed the greater part of Asia in establishing itself in its present domain.

The question of why animals penetrate certain regions and not others near by, poses a fascinating problem for the naturalist. Barriers are chiefly climatic or physical. When they are impassable—like the edges of oceans—accidents or factors outside the "laws of Nature" may eventually permit some species to pass across. (Thus, for example, the wild dogs known as dingoes appear to have reached Australia in the boats of ancient man.) The genet, on the other hand, has, or seems to have, a full visaed passport to Asia—yet somewhere there is a taboo around most of that continent, keeping the animal out. Possibly the competition of native species is the decisive element here, but it is not obviously so.

A HUNTER OF SMALL GAME

All the genets are night prowlers, lying up during daylight hours in hollow trees, a crevice in the rocks, or a burrow in the ground. After nightfall the long, lithe body weaves through tall grass and thickets like a snake. More often the animal is glimpsed in the trees. Once in a while it may be seen before the sun has actually set, travelling either singly or in pairs; it moves cautiously, preferring dark, shady places where rocks and bushes provide cover. A home-loving creature, the genet returns daily to the same hideaway.

THE GENET—WEASEL CAT OF AFRICA

Though nothing seems to bar its entry into Asia, the genet has mysteriously refrained from settling there, except in certain southern parts. Its main home is Africa, but it is also found in southern Europe. A fierce little rat and mouse killer, the genet has unsheathed claws with which it attacks its victims.

The genet is above all a small-game hunter. It seeks out rats and mice that prowl about the jungle floor. It will devour any reptiles or insects that cross its path, and climbs about in the trees and thickets in search of small birds roosting there. Remains of hares and guinea fowl have been found outside its den and it is well known as a raider of chicken pens. On occasion it goes for bigger game.

When cornered, a genet will put up a good fight, growling and spitting like a house cat. It can slash out with its claws faster than the eye can follow. Still, it is no match for a dog. It has a reasonably long life expectancy, and has been known to reach twelve years of age.

There is no fixed breeding season among the genets, nor do they bear large families. Two or three is about the average for a litter. Almost any kind of retreat will serve as a nursery, so long as it is safe, warm and dry.

As we find in most other kinds of animals, there are several species. Africa has a number of varieties such as the Leopard Genet, the Tiger Genet, and the Crested Genet. All are more or less conspicuously marked and coloured as the popular names indicate. They are variations of the European Genet, *Genetta*. The genet of southern Europe was used as a domestic cat by the ancient Greeks and as late as the sixteenth century was common and tame in such cities as Constantinople.

LINSANGS—HANDSOME TREE "CATS" OF THE JUNGLE

The linsangs are the most catlike of all the weasel cats. These creatures of tropical Asia and the East Indies rather resemble the genets in general form, only they are somewhat smaller—about fifteen or sixteen inches is the average length, plus a tail almost as long again. They are handsome fellows, too—the Spotted Linsang's slender body and superb tail are golden brown with a bold pattern of large black spots; the Banded Linsang has five broad bands running across its body, and the tail is banded with alternate dark and light markings.

Linsangs live by hunting live game, and will disdain any food except meat. Though appearing to be better suited for travel on the ground, like the genets they are extremely active in the trees. They breed twice a year—once in February and again in August. The babies come two to the litter as a rule, and are born in a hollow tree, so far as we know.

The linsangs got their name from the Javanese. The animals make up the genus *Prionodon*, which means "saw-tooth"; the teeth

[5-7]

Hyenas are noted as eaters of carrion, but they rarely have a chance of this kind of food. Vultures are so quick to discover and feast upon dead animals that all the hyenas find is bones. Fortunately their teeth and jaws are powerful enough to crack and crunch these last remains. The hyena is also noted for the chilling, diabolical caricature of the human laugh it utters when approaching a carcass.   *See page 550*

Hyena pups are born seal brown in colour without any markings. A litter is composed of two, three or four pups. With practically no natural enemies under normal conditions, the hyena has a comparatively long life expectancy.
See page 550

[5-7A]

The grey wild cat is the common wild cat of Africa from Egypt to the
Cape of Good Hope. If it looks like the house variety, there is a good
reason: some strains of our domestic cat were derived from its ancestors.
See page 563

[5-8]

Scarcity of food makes life in the wild hard for the Canadian lynx. It
will sometimes supplement its snowshoe rabbit diet with beaver and,
when the small game supply runs low, will stalk deer. At the crucial
moment a lynx strikes with unbelievable swiftness.   *See page 564*

[5-8A]

[5-9]

Smaller than the Canadian lynx, the bay lynx or bobcat resembles it in many respects, including the uncatlike indifference to water. Ranging from Southern Canada to Mexico and feeding on rats, mice and snakes (and sometimes poultry and small domestic stock) as well as rabbits, the bobcat has a little easier time of it. The lynx family is noted for its keen eyesight. See page 565

[5-10]

A pair of young lionesses share a meal. The only sociable cats, lions prefer to travel in groups, except during the mating season. A lion never destroys another animal for the fun of it—it kills only when it must eat, and it eats all of what it kills before striking again. *See page 580*

really do look jagged and sawlike. The so-called African Linsang, *Poiana*, of the Congo, is in reality a small genet with a spotted coat like the rest of the genets.

IT TAKES TO TREES LIKE A CAT

The weasel-cat family has certain distinguishing features—a foxlike face, short legs, a long body like a weasel, and the tail and temperament of a cat. The banded linsang of Asia and the East Indies follows this description, but is more catlike in its habits than any other member of the family. Like the felines, it spends much of its time in trees and, appropriately enough, it feeds on birds.

CIVET CATS—THE SKUNKS' OLD WORLD RIVALS

A good many of the readers of this book will never have heard of the civet cats before encountering them here. That is not surprising, for these weasel cats, like the others, make their home in the warmer parts of the Old World. Small carnivores, they prowl the jungle land at night. Even naturalists do not know too much about their intimate home life.

In their native regions, the civet cats are important for two chief reasons. First of all, they unwittingly serve as foresters, being instrumental in the planting of trees. In addition to flesh, civets eat fruits and berries. They do not digest the seeds. These are distributed over

EAL / 5—D

a considerable distance, where they germinate and eventually grow into trees.

But this helpful work is not the main source of the civets' value to mankind. The animals' name comes from an Arabic word, *zabad*, which refers to a scent—civet—extracted from the musk glands. A good commercial price is set upon civet, this substance being used extensively in the Orient as a basis for perfume and as a drug.

THE SCENT OF THE CIVET CAT

There is nothing mysterious about the civet or secretion. It is made up of free ammonia, resin, fat, and volatile oil, and is located in a double-pocket pouch under the skin of the animal's abdomen, with an opening near the tail. The natives insert a spoon in this opening and extract the jelly-like dark yellow substance. This sounds easy to do, yet requires much skill; the civet cat not only possesses sharp teeth but it is strong and agile as well, and can inflict nasty scratches with its claws. (The animals, of course, are kept in cages.) The musk is extracted every fourteen or twenty days.

In nature, the civet cat uses its musk glands for scenting tree trunks, the ground, and similar objects, as a means of communication, so that members of a species will be able to find each other at night in a dark forest. Like most night-prowling animals, the civet cats—so far as we know—are generally silent and might have a difficult time keeping in touch with one another if they lacked the scent.

The larger carnivores occasionally attack civet cats. In such an emergency, some of them will suddenly and unexpectedly discharge their evil-smelling, burning secretion into the face of the foe. This frustrates the attacker long enough for the civet to escape.

The civet cats possess yet another protective device which reminds us further of the skunks, those other adepts in gas warfare. Civet cats are strikingly marked, so that they can be easily recognized, remembered, and avoided by would-be enemies.

SOME WELL-KNOWN CIVET CATS

One of the best known of these weasel cats—and an excellent producer of civet—is the civet cat of India and the Orient. This big creature (it has a head-and-body length of two feet, plus a tail one and one-half feet long) is easy to identify: it has a full, black-and-white-ringed tail, and many ill-defined dark markings on its grizzled body;

across the throat there runs a broad black band, set off by areas of white. A prominent crest of long erectile hairs extends down the middle of the back. To complete this striking picture, the feet are black. The fur of this heavy-bodied animal (the Oriental civet may weigh twenty-five pounds) is thick and soft, making it of considerable importance to the fur trade.

All the civet cats have well-developed musk glands, and the Rasse, *Viverricula*, a smaller species of eastern Asia, has been introduced into Madagascar, Socotra, and other islands for the sake of its scent. The African Civet, *Civettictis*, is much like the large Oriental species both in size and markings but its fur is coarse and limp—it is used commercially only for trimming cloth coats. This animal is probably the "sentoivane" of African folklore—the mysterious creature whose hairs are said to be used by witch doctors to dye milk red.

A CIVET THAT FISHES

There is a fisherman among the civets, a beautiful species with a dark chestnut-brown body, white lips and throat, and a bushy reddish tail. The Water Civet, *Osbornictis*, catches fish in the rivers and streams that thread through the jungles of the Congo. It has sharp teeth for holding its slippery finny prey and the soles of the feet are naked for easy travel on mud flats. (In other civets the soles are more or less hairy.)

THE PALM CIVETS

So far we have had the civets that live on the ground and feed largely by hunting small animal life. The palm civets (there are several kinds in Asia and Africa) live in the trees and subsist largely on fruit. One, the Asiatic Palm Civet, *Paradoxurus*, is known throughout India and Ceylon as the "toddy cat"—it is especially fond of toddy, the juice of the palm tree, which it drinks from the vessels attached to the trees by the natives to receive the liquid.

Like all the palm civets, this one is a creature of the night, and lies up during the day curled in a ball among the fronds of palm trees. Mango groves are also one of its favourite resorts; it not infrequently haunts human habitations and sleeps in thatched roofs.

The Otter Civet or Mampalon, *Cynogale*, of the Malay region, is the only civet that has really taken to the water while retaining its tree-climbing habits. It has the flat head, broad toes and feet, and thick, dense fur of an aquatic animal. It swims and fishes like an otter and is as much at home in the water as on dry land.

THE ONLY CIVET CAT WITH A GRASPING TAIL

All civet cats have bushy tails, but none can compare with the strong, useful one of the tree-dwelling binturong of Asia. Its tail—almost as long as the binturong's entire body— is used for grasping and hanging from trees. Equally unique is the animal's raucous howl, for civet cats are usually silent creatures. To compensate for their lack of voice, they spread the secretions of their musk glands along forest byways to communicate with one another.

Most remarkable of the Asiatic civets is the Binturong, *Arctictis*. This lop-eared creature resembles a large palm civet—it is over two feet long, with a tail of almost the same length—and wears a black, shaggy coat. But its most outstanding peculiarity is the lengthy, powerful tail. Like the monkeys of South America, the binturong can hang by its tail or possibly use it as a fifth hand, a great convenience for an animal that lives in the trees.

The binturong is at home in the forests of Assam and west to the Philippines, including Sumatra and Borneo. It appears to be the only noisy member of the civet group. Its loud howls, we are told, will often shatter the relative quiet of the jungle night.

CURIOUS CIVET CATS OF MADAGASCAR

Madagascar is noted for its many strange, primitive forms of animal life (the lemurs and tenrecs are some others we have already looked at), and not the least curious among them are the local weasel cats. Several are exceedingly graceful animals, no larger than rats. One, the agile little Vontsira, *Galidia*, has a bright reddish-brown coat and a bushy tail and bounds about in the trees just like a squirrel during the daytime. The Striped Madagascar Civet, *Galidictis*, is ornately marked with six or eight black stripes down the back; there are several species, with narrow or broad stripes, and these animals are of some economic value as mouse-catchers.

AN ODDITY AMONG CIVET CATS

Civet cats are amazingly diversified in habit and structure. A case in point is the falanouc of Madagascar, which has switched from flesh-eating to a diet of insects and fruit. Notice that its muzzle is very narrow and slender and that it has delicate jaws.

There are still other civet oddities in Madagascar. One of the most interesting is the Falanouc, *Eupleres*. This creature offers a remarkable instance of a carnivorous animal that has given up a flesh diet and taken to eating insects and soft fruit; its teeth and jaws are extremely small and weak. For the rest, it is a large, brown, fuzzy-haired animal about the size of a house cat, with a bottle-brush of a tail.

The Foussa, *Fossa*, is another strange Malagasy civet. A robust animal with four black lines down the back, it feeds on insects and lizards. It should not be confused with the fossa, which is described later.

MONGOOSES—EXPERT SNAKE-KILLERS

The mongoose, a long-bodied, weasel-like animal with a lengthy, bushy tail, is famed as a killer of snakes. Although no larger than a house cat, it will engage even a seven-foot foe. It does not generally seek combat with reptiles, but, when hungry, it needs no other incentive to attack them. In southern Asia and in Africa, where poisonous snakes abound, the mongoose is one of the commonest of carnivores.

An experienced old mongoose will quickly kill a cobra. Like a clever boxer, it provokes the deadly snake to strike—but the uncanny, expert judgment and sharp reflexes of the mongoose enable it to dance away unharmed. Time and again the snake lashes out and misses. (In the battle the mongoose carries the stiff hairs of its body and tail at right angles, which makes the animal appear larger; presumably this is a factor in causing the snake to strike short.)

Each time the reptile drops to the ground fully extended at the end of its strike, the mongoose springs in and attempts to sink its teeth into the back of its enemy's head. Finally it inflicts a fatal wound, and the mongoose eats the snake, head first, including the poison glands. When fully gorged, it lies down to sleep; it resumes the feast on awakening.

Sometimes, to be sure, the mongoose takes a beating. The natives of the tropical lands where the animal dwells say that it retires to the jungle after being bitten by a venomous snake and eats certain roots as an antidote for the poison. Such stories are without foundation. The mongoose is not immune to the snake's venom, and it takes the greatest care to avoid being bitten. When artificially injected, the poison is fatal.

However, there are mongooses and mongooses, and some of them give us reason to assume that they are better able to withstand the bite of a venomous snake than are many other animals. In a staged fight between a large cobra and a mongoose, the latter survived although apparently severely bitten on several occasions by the cobra. This mongoose did not seem particularly interested in avoiding the strike of the cobra or in seizing it by the head. It bit the snake whenever the opportunity offered and at one time seized it by the lower jaw. The possibility exists that the mongoose, through its constant eating of snakes, may occasionally acquire some degree of immunity against the poison.

ONE OF THE WORLD'S BEST SNAKE-KILLERS

The brave and cocky little mongoose may be only two feet long—yet it will attack and kill a seven-foot poisonous snake. It is also one of the most effective natural enemies of mice, rats, and scorpions, and by cutting down their numbers performs a vitally important service to man. Unfortunately, the animal can lose its popularity and usefulness by attacking poultry; imported into the West Indies, it has become a nuisance. The Indian mongoose is the "Rikki-tikki-tavi" of Kipling's famous tale in *The Jungle Book*.

The mongoose is capable of killing any creature up to its own size. Besides reptiles, it feeds on birds, insects, rats, and similar animals. More active by day than by night, it usually hunts in the early mornings and late evenings, though it may be about during the midday heat and at any hour of the night.

This animal is interesting to watch. It has a habit of stopping frequently to glance around with its sharp red eyes or to listen with its head cocked to one side and one foot raised; it seems always ready to dart at any lurking prey or to scurry off if alarmed. When cornered, it can climb, but it rarely does so. Its long claws are more suited for digging than for climbing trees.

Despite its naturally savage disposition, the mongoose may be tamed. Taken young and treated properly, it can be handled without fear and will keep buildings free of rats. Sometimes it enters people's houses without invitation, and becomes part of the family. It will live on friendly terms with dogs and cats but can seldom be taught not to kill poultry.

The mongoose was introduced into the West Indies and Hawaii, where it has unfortunately become a menace to chickens and many other harmless and desirable animals. It was brought in to destroy the rats which infest the islands, but the rats have found a way to meet this threat; they now live in the trees, where they are safe from the mongoose.

Mongooses in a general way resemble the civets and genets but their claws cannot be drawn in like a cat's. Possessing a comparatively lengthy and hairy tail, a pointed face, and low rounded ears, they do not, like the civets, have scent glands. The fur is usually a grizzled brown or black.

MANY KINDS OF MONGOOSES

Europe's Only Mongoose. The warmer regions of the earth are the home of many different types of mongoose, each with its own peculiarities. Only one kind of mongoose lives in Europe—southern Spain to be exact.

This creature, which is also found in great numbers all over southern Asia and most of Africa, is the Common Mongoose, *Herpestes*. A slender animal, it measures close to two feet in head and body; its tapered tail is several inches shorter. It has short legs, with large feet, and its head is rather small and pointed. The woolly coat is a uniform mixture of pale buff and black, except for the tip of the tail, which is all black.

The Crab-eating Mongoose. In Asia we find the Crab-eating Mongoose, *Herpestes urva,* a large creature with long, thick fur like that of a woodchuck or badger. Grey in colour, it has a horizontal white stripe on each side of the neck and its feet are blackish brown. It weighs up to six pounds. The crab-eating mongoose frequents watercourses, where it feeds on crabs, frogs, and small rodents, and sometimes goes fishing in the water.

The Indian Mongoose. In India, Assam, and Afghanistan dwells a smaller species, the Indian Mongoose, *Herpestes edwardsii.* It weighs about three pounds, and its colour is iron grey. The young, three or four in number, are born in holes dug in the ground by the adults. It is the Indian mongoose that was introduced into many of the West Indies Islands. These animals became so numerous at Botany Bay, St. Thomas, that two or three individuals would fight over table scraps thrown to them.

"The Tracker". One of the largest of the mongooses is the Grey Mongoose, or Ichneumon, *Herpestes ichneumon,* found pretty much

THE INQUISITIVE MONGOOSE

The mongoose is enormously curious about people, their activities and their belongings. Unless it is discouraged, it will approach human beings in order to watch them at close hand. Should a bright piece of jewellery catch its eye, this mischievous sneak thief may grab it and run off. Above is the Malagasy mongoose, one of Madagascar's striped varieties.

throughout Africa. Its over-all length is forty-four inches; about half of this is the black-tipped tail. The grey mongoose normally travels about singly or in pairs, but as many as fourteen have been seen hunting in a pack.

This large mongoose preys on small mammals, reptiles, frogs, fish, and fresh-water crustaceans. It got its name "ichneumon" ("the tracker") because it was believed to be especially fond of crocodile eggs, hunting them assiduously. Revered by the ancient Egyptians, it was frequently mummified.

Africa's Horde of Mongooses. Africa has many other species. The large White-tailed Mongoose, *Ichneumia*, of the central and southern regions, does not always have on its tail the white tip for which the animal is named, but may be quite blackish all over. It spends the day in its hole in the ground, coming out at night to prey upon birds and small mammals. The Marsh Mongoose, *Atilax*, a large, brownish creature, swims and dives well in the lakes and marshes it frequents, and feeds upon much the same kind of food as the ichneumon.

Striped mongooses exist in many forms, and the Banded or Zebra Mongoose, *Mungos mungo*, can readily be recognized by the numerous thin bands of alternating light buff and dark brown that cross its lower back and fade into finely mixed buff and black on its shoulders. This is a rather small creature that prefers to roam abroad during daylight. It goes about in troops of six or more and is most abundant near rivers and marshes. Its typical diet consists principally of insect life such as termites, beetles, and cockroaches.

When Nature permits a creature to multiply greatly, as it has the mongoose, we often find it in many different sizes, some considerably smaller than others. The Dwarf Mongoose, *Helogale*, measures ten inches or less from nose to rump, and the tail is about eight inches long; this animal is coloured dark brown finely mixed with yellow. The dwarf mongoose travels about during the day, hunting in packs of fifteen or more. Largely an eater of insects, it varies its diet with fruits and small mammals.

A pretty little South African creature is the Suricate, or Slender-tailed Meerkat, *Suricata*. It is light grey or pale buff, with broken dark bands crossing its lower back. This inhabitant of the grass veldt and arid plains dwells sociably in burrows, from which it emerges in the daytime to sit up on its haunches like a ground squirrel, and look curiously about. Insects make up the greater part of its diet. It is often tamed.

FOSSAS—THE BIG CATS OF MADAGASCAR

The Fossa, *Cryptoprocta*, once enjoyed a reputation for great ferocity —so much so that the single species in existence was named *Cryptoprocta ferox*. Occasionally there are reports that this sharp-clawed catlike animal attacks sheep and young cattle, and it is well known to the natives of Madagascar because of its raids on their chickens. But the old tales that ascribed to the fossa the bloodthirstiness of the lion and tiger are nowadays taken with a generous sprinkling of salt.

The fossa is a curiosity among the carnivores. This one species comprises a whole subfamily in the animal kingdom and appears to

A KILLER IN FABLE BUT NOT IN FACT

The fossa, a big flesh-eating cat of Madagascar, has been falsely likened to the tiger in savagery. However, any true account of its so-called ferocity reveals only run-of-the-mill attacks on poultry, sheep, and young cattle. The five-foot-long fossa seems to represent a half-way mark between the civet cat and the true cat.

represent a bridge between the weasel cat family and the true cats. Harsh short fur, reddish brown or brownish grey in hue, covers its slender body. The legs are short and the body appears very long because it is so slender. (Actually, the animal may reach a total length of five feet, with the well-haired tail almost half of this.) The claws are needle-sharp and hooked like those of a cat; the fossa can draw them in and out, too. On the ground it walks on the soles of its feet, whereas the cats, as we shall soon see, move about on their toes.

The trees are home to the agile fossa, which inhabits the rain-forests of eastern Madagascar as well as the drier forests of the west. Here it preys upon birds and lemurs. It is most active at night, but is sometimes seen abroad in the early morning or late evening. Mostly it keeps to itself.

The fossa is the largest carnivore in Madagascar, where it takes the place of the big cats.

Hyenas and Aardwolves—Eaters of Carrion

HYENAS—THE BONE-CRUNCHERS

HYENAS scour the plains throughout Africa, Palestine, Arabia, and India in search of animal remains. These sturdy, unhandsome beasts are the bone-crunchers of the animal kingdom. Their teeth are massive and their jaws powerful enough to crack and crush the thigh bones of large animals like the zebra and even the buffalo.

Such eating equipment has its uses. Most people believe that hyenas are exclusively eaters of carrion. As a rule, however, few dead animals ever reach the actual putrefying carrion stage on the plains of Africa; often the best a hyena can expect is a feast of bones, which is apparently quite acceptable.

On one occasion, in Kenya, the author checked the time it took Nature to dispose of a dead animal. Five minutes after a zebra had been shot and killed, the first scout vulture came. In ten minutes there were thirty vultures feeding on the zebra, and twenty minutes later only the bones and the hide remained. About this time—it was late in the evening—two hyenas located the kill. By next morning nothing was left of the dead zebra.

Equipped with a keen sense of smell, the hyena can detect a carcass many miles away. It makes for any spot over which vultures are flying, being assured of the presence of a dead animal. To a large extent it depends on the kills left by lions and by troops of wild dogs. Lack of speed prevents the hyena from becoming an habitual game destroyer but it will kill domestic stock.

Despite its powerful jaws and teeth, the hyena rarely attempts to defend itself. When cornered, it will try to escape rather than fight for its freedom. If escape is not possible, it will play dead until its attackers drop their guard. Then it springs to its feet and dashes off.

Most hunters consider the hyena one of the most degraded of animals. That the beast is reluctant to devour its own kind seems to indicate that it does have a moral standard. It is surprisingly free from body odours, and smells much sweeter than a lion or a jackal. In fact, the natives readily eat the meat of the hyena and are keen to get the heart, believing that it will bring them courage. This is rather strange, since, as we have seen, the hyena seldom puts up a fight when the odds are against it, and is generally referred to as a coward.

Prehistoric Europe knew the hyena well. Once it haunted caverns as far west as England, leaving behind it a curious trail, much as it does today. The dung of the hyena dries into hard white balls chiefly composed of bone fragments. They are almost indestructible, and have been found fossilized in the caves that were tenanted by these extinct forms of hyena thousands of years ago.

LAUGHING HYENAS—BEASTS OF MIGHT AND MAGIC

The Spotted Hyena, or Laughing Hyena, *Crocuta crocuta*, is the largest and strongest of the scavengers. A full-grown spotted hyena may stand from two and one-half to three feet at the shoulders and measure as much as five and one-half feet in head-and-body length. Some weigh up to 175 pounds.

This robust carnivore is as hideous as its reputation. It has a broad, ugly face, large, rounded ears, a short tail, and heavy limbs. The coarse, scanty fur is grey or buff in colour, with a good many irregular blotches of brown or black. Even the posture of the hyena is ungraceful: the animal's front limbs are longer than its hind ones, and the body slopes downward from the high neck and shoulders to the foot-long coarse-haired tail.

The peculiarities of the hyena do not end here. Unlike most four-footed creatures, it does not trot, but paces—that is, the fore and hind limbs on each side of the body move forward together, producing a rolling gait much like that of the camel.

Under normal conditions the hyena does not hunt living healthy game but follows great herds of zebra and antelope and attacks the sick, the weak, the maimed, the aged, and the young. Where civilization has driven big game from large areas and the hyena is left without its natural prey, it will attack domestic sheep and cattle, but only when driven by extreme hunger. Possessed of extraordinary vitality, it can drag a two-hundred-pound carcass as much as one hundred yards.

The hyena's gluttony, like its strength, is proverbial. Theodore Roosevelt tells of finding a hyena trapped inside a dead elephant. It had crept inside the carcass and gorged itself with so much flesh from the walls of the elephant's stomach that it was too fat to get out the way it had entered.

Daytime is for slumber, so far as the hyena is concerned. Its home is a burrow in the ground or a dark cave in the rocks. It is a heavy sleeper, and can be approached quite closely without being disturbed. Usually it lives in hilly territory on the margins of desert country, and descends to the plains to look for food at sunset, but first it visits a nearby pool to drink. Then the hunt begins.

THE HYENA'S LAUGH

Scarcely a night passes on the African veldt when a traveller will not hear the strange cry of the prowling bone-crusher. Its voice is extraordinary and the sounds it produces are legion.

The hyena's characteristic howl is a crescendo beginning on a low, mournful tone and ending with a shrill, high-pitched note. When the animal approaches a carcass it utters an entirely different cry, the weirdest of all. It is a chilling, diabolical caricature of the human laugh, a hysterical cackle, which has earned the name of "laughing hyena" for this beast. The hyena is a ventriloquist, and the sound offers little clue as to the exact whereabouts of the animal.

Although the hyena is solitary in its habits, when a kill is made or found, as many as nineteen or twenty of the animals may gather. Their loud quarrelling over the food carries far through the night.

THE EVIL-LOOKING HYENA

Hyenas have the unflattering distinction of being among the most gruesome members of the animal kingdom, in appearance as well as habits. They prey upon feeble, injured, or old animals; when attacked themselves, they feign death in order to avoid fighting. Though a well-known eater of carrion, the hyena often finds a carcass only after the vultures have already picked it clean of flesh. With its powerful teeth, the hyena finishes the job by chewing up the bones. Pictured above is the spotted or laughing hyena.

HYENA FACT AND LEGEND

The spotted hyena is very bold at night and for this reason it is much feared. Accounts have greatly exaggerated its size and ferociousness and given rise to widespread belief in an uncanny creature known as the Nandi bear or chimiset. In different parts of the country this strange beast may go under other names as well, but most of the tales about it follow the same pattern. They tell of a bloodthirsty animal with long, grizzly hair—an animal that attacks natives at night, either mauling them badly or killing them. It is supposed to leave a very large footprint. Many white people are convinced that this weird creature really prowls about the African jungles, but it is totally unknown to science.

Still, in all these stories a certain amount of fact gleams through —enough to illuminate the hyena and its deeds. Although the spotted hyena will rarely attack people during the day, things are different after sundown. On hot nights the natives often sleep out in the open and there are many cases where they have actually been attacked by hyenas. The animals usually go for the face; it is not too uncommon to see natives that have been mauled and frightfully scarred by such an assault.

Also, it is a common practice in many parts of Asia and Africa for natives to move aged people, about to die, out of their huts and villages. Being superstitious about death, the natives never let it happen in their dwellings. The old people are left to meet their end out in the open, and we cannot be surprised if the hyena does not turn up its nose at such golden opportunities. Many times the beast has been reported as a grave-robber.

DEATH OF A HYENA

Hyenas are often reputed to commit gruesome acts upon their own bodies. One of the most horrible sights the author has ever witnessed met his eyes when he came out of the brush one day just as a hunter shot a hyena. The bullet struck the beast in the abdomen and ripped it open. The hyena, as we have remarked, is noted for its unusual vitality. This animal, though mortally wounded, continued to gallop away. Without stopping, it reached back and snapped off the protruding intestines, which only dragged out more.

The author saw this awful performance repeated time and again. The animal never paused in its headlong rush even though two more bullets entered its side; finally a fourth shot in the shoulder put the creature out of its misery.

Such behaviour, unnatural as it may seem to us, is no oddity in Nature. It is by no means restricted to the hyena. The author once saw a red squirrel almost disembowel itself before it could be killed outright. In this case it seemed that the animal considered the protruding intestines as a foreign object attached to its abdomen, and the cause of its pain.

There is nothing unusual in the fact, sometimes commented upon

[5-11]

A large male lion may weigh 500 pounds and measure over seven feet in length. Highly intelligent and inclined to be friendly, lions as a rule respect men; the man-killer is a rare but serious menace and is hunted down and exterminated as quickly as possible.   *See page 580*

[5-11A]

Cheetahs hunt by sight rather than smell and unlike many of the cat family roam about during the daylight hours. Marked with solid black spots instead of the rosettes typical of true leopards, cheetahs in a restful mood purr like house cats.   *See page 595*

[5-12]

The cougar has enormous power concealed in its lithe six-foot body: it can spring twenty feet in one leap. Its weird drawn-out shriek is considered the wildest, most hair-raising sound of the American wilderness. *See page 573*

Originally panthers and leopards were thought to be two distinct animals but the difference turned out to be a matter of size and sex, the male the panther and the female the leopard. This "kitten" will grow to an overall length of about seven feet. *See page 576*

[5-12A]

with astonishment, that a hyena will chew its foot off when caught in a trap; here again, most animals will do the same, and the action is easily explained. The pressure from the jaws of the trap cuts off circulation, and the paw soon becomes numb. Thus the animal is quite unaware that it is biting its own foot off in its effort to escape.

AN ODD FEMALE

One marked peculiarity of the spotted hyenas is that the female exceeds the male in size. To this the female has added another oddity: her sexual organs are quite exceptional in structure and closely resemble those of the male in outward appearance. This phenomenon, unique among the carnivores, is not found in other hyenas. It has given rise to a native superstition that the spotted hyena can assume the role of male or female at will; many white people also hold this belief.

Of course some animals do change their sex—certain snails and fishes are famous in this respect. But, up until the present, the scientific world has greeted with scepticism any claim that a mammal of one sex could alter in its characteristics enough to breed as a member of the other sex. There just has not been sufficiently convincing proof presented.

Of great interest, however, is certain evidence concerning the spotted hyena. C. E. Fronk, M.D., of the Fronk Clinic, Honolulu, while hunting in Tanganyika not long ago, shot a full-grown male spotted hyena which, on dissection of its sexual organs, revealed rudimentary female organs, he reports. A second specimen he shot was a well-developed female that revealed rudimentary male organs. A third full-grown animal showed equally rudimentary organs of both male and female, neither sex being dominant at the time. A Mr. Carr Hartley of Tanganyika further states that one living hyena in his possession has both fathered and mothered at least one litter of puppies. This report has strengthened the growing supposition.

It is possible that the doctor was mistaken in his assumption that the animals he examined were adult. A report, based on observations on mating spotted hyenas in zoological gardens, by Karl M. Schreeder, published in 1952, seems to prove conclusively that this animal is not bisexual.

In embryo, a mammal is potentially both male and female; as it develops, one sex becomes dominant. Nature has her imperfect products, and there may be signs of maleness and femaleness together in one animal. Such a creature is never capable of the functions of both sexes, and is usually incapable of the functions of either.

YOUNG HYENAS

The nursery for the young hyenas is a large hole in the ground. The pups, numbering two to four in a litter, are born in March or April, about three months after mating time. They are seal brown in colour, without any spots or stripes. After a month or two the fur becomes lighter in patches, leaving the characteristic dark spots. It is questionable whether the male plays an active part in bringing up the family.

Under natural conditions the spotted hyena has practically no enemies and has a long life expectancy. One lived twenty-five years in a zoo. Taken young, hyenas make docile pets, and become quite attached to their owners.

The spotted hyena is found throughout Africa from Ethiopia and Senegal south to the Cape of Good Hope. There is only one species, but six varying forms occur in different regions.

STRIPED HYENAS

In India, Palestine, Arabia, and North Africa to Tanganyika we encounter another common type, the Striped Hyena, *Hyaena hyaena*. It is smaller than the spotted hyena, its head and body length being about three and one-half feet, and its tail one and one-half feet long; the average weight is about seventy-four pounds. This animal is soiled greyish in colour with narrow tawny and blackish stripes running across the body and legs. Its life habits are much the same as those of the spotted hyena.

BROWN HYENAS

An interesting example of how an animal takes up a specialized kind of existence is shown by the Brown Hyena, *Hyaena brunnea*, also known as the Strand Wolf or Strandjut. This South African species (it does not range north of the Zambesi River) haunts the beaches and shorelines, where it feeds on marine refuse. It is more timid and retiring than the spotted hyena, and is not likely to attack human beings. Although best known as a haunter of seashores, it also occurs far inland.

The brown hyena is a little smaller and more lightly built than the spotted hyena. Nevertheless, it is a powerful brute, and one of its kind caught in a trap lugged away the sixty-pound log to which the mechanism was attached, dragging it four miles during one night —faster, for a short distance, than a man could run, hampered with this impediment.

For a hyena, this one has extremely long hair (about ten inches) on its back. It has a coarse blackish-grey coat, and stripes only on the legs.

AARDWOLVES—AFRICAN TERMITE-EATERS

The Aardwolf, *Proteles cristatus*, looks like a small hyena, but it is very mild and inoffensive in its character. Common through South

THE HYENA'S MEEK RELATIVE

Despite its name, the aardwolf is related to hyenas, not wolves. Its appearance is deceptive for though it looks like a small hyena, this timid creature prefers to feed on insects. When menaced, it bristles its mane and ejects an offensive-smelling fluid from its anal glands. The name "aardwolf" is Dutch for "earth wolf"—derived from the aardwolf's habit of making its home in burrows.

and East Africa, and north to Somalia, it lives in open sandy plains, scrubby brush country, and rocky hills.

For the aardwolf, a hole in the ground is home. This "earth" is sometimes dug by the animal itself, but more often it moves into a deserted ant-bear's den. Now and then a number of aardwolves may dwell in the same burrow. It was because of the animal's habit of living in the ground that it acquired its Dutch name, aardwolf ("earth wolf"). It is not a wolf but, as its appearance and posture suggest, a close relative of the hyena.

Because the aardwolf spends the day underground, it is frequently overlooked in places where it is quite abundant in numbers. It has a pointed muzzle and large, erect ears. Its long fur is coarse in texture; it is light grey or buff in colour, with bands of dark brown running across the back.

The word *cristatus*, in the aardwolf's scientific name, means "crested", and this creature has a sort of mane—a distinct crest of long hairs running down the back. When attacked, the aardwolf erects its mane. This gives the animal a formidable appearance that belies its essentially timid nature. Under provocation, the aardwolf also emits a malodorous fluid from its anal glands.

An animal's teeth will tell you much about how it gains its livelihood. The aardwolf's mouth is quite unlike the hyena's: the jaws are weak, the teeth small. This is hardly the equipment for a tearer of flesh, much less a cruncher of bones, and in fact the aardwolf is rather specialized to an insect diet. When the aardwolf sets forth on its nightly hunts, much of the food it seeks is white ants, which it consumes in great masses. Other insects and scraps from kills left by the larger carnivores round out the aardwolf's diet.

Aardwolves bear their young in a burrow in November or December. There are two to four babies in one litter, and more than one female and her young may occupy the same den. The aardwolf is fairly sociable, and packs of half a dozen or more may travel about in search of food, though pairs of hunters or single hunters are equally common. The aardwolf's cry is much like the hyena's.

In South Africa, hunting the aardwolf with dogs has been a popular sport for many years. The animal is not fleet of foot and the dogs overtake it easily. The aardwolf must depend upon ruse to save itself; it often escapes its pursuers by dodging and doubling back over its tracks in the low bush.

In zoos the aardwolf, or maanhaar-jackal as it is sometimes called, has lived up to thirteen years. Only one species exists, with six geographical forms. The animal is a little more than two feet long and it has a bushy tail some six inches in length. At the shoulders it stands about twenty inches. The genus name, *Proteles*, means "forward perfect"—the aardwolf's forefeet, following the basic mammal pattern, have five toes, whereas the hyena only has four on each foot. With the hyenas, the aardwolves make up the family Hyaenidae.

The Cats—Stalkers and Springers

THE CATS, from the tabby to the tiger, are a bundle of high-tension muscles, ever ready to explode into action. At rest they offer a perfect picture of complacency and relaxation. They purr, they are soft and peaceful. But in a fraction of a second they may be transformed into snarling, slashing terrors—vibrant machines of destruction, energy on the loose.

Cats are springers. Just as dogs are runners, relying upon sustained speed to overtake and bring down their prey, cats are masters of the art of leaping. From a running, walking, standing, or sitting position, they can suddenly catapult themselves into the air and hit their quarry with a stunning impact. They land with claws extended and jaws wide open, teeth bared ready to sink into the victim's throat.

A CAT'S CLAWS

In the world of flesh-eaters, the cats (family Felidae) are the masters of their trade. They have the longest and sharpest canine teeth of all the carnivores. In cutting through flesh and sinew, the side teeth operate like shears: the knifelike edges in each jaw slice up and down, cut past each other, but do not meet. (There are, in the mouth of a cat, no bone-crushing teeth such as we find in a dog or a bear.) The tongue is wonderfully fitted to help out. Its upper surface is rasplike, and the largest cats will draw blood by merely licking the surface of the skin.

Cats have the sharpest claws of all the mammals. Perfect cutting tools, they are compressed on each side and hooked. With the exception of the cheetah's, the claws of the cats are retractile—that is, they can be withdrawn at will into sheaths in the paws, or they can be extended for action. Thus the animals can trot along silently on their foot pads, keeping the claws safely protected, then bring them out as sharp as ever when there is work for them to do. A dog's claws are always extended.

EXQUISITELY KEEN SENSES

All this marvellous equipment for getting their livelihood would be worth little to the cats, which hunt mostly at night, if they could not detect their prey at a distance. Here, too, Nature has not left them in the lurch. They have moist noses, like dogs, and can smell and hear extremely well.

In a cat's ears there are hairs that catch minute vibrations in the air and tell the animal of movements it has not even seen. Its whiskers are also sensitive feelers that work in much the same way, registering the slightest contact at the tip, and transmitting the sensation to the nerves at the root.

SEEING IN THE DARK

Everyone knows that cats—tame or wild—can see in the dark. But just how do they do it? What, too, is the cause of the familiar green glare in the eyes of cats at night?

This glare is known as eyeshine. The lining at the back of a cat's eye is coated with masses of minute particles called guanin, which have a metallic lustre of silver or gold. When light strikes the guanin, the particles amplify and brighten the dimly lighted picture focused on the mirror or retina inside the eye, thus affording better visibility.

The slightest trace of light is caught by the guanin, and a glow is created by it.

The purpose of guanin is not to reflect light and illuminate the outside world. It is only when bright artificial light is suddenly directed into the eyes of a cat at night that the over-abundance or surplus of light is reflected back. Given time, the luminative particles will retreat into their cells and the eyeshine will stop.

The dark pupils of the cat's eyes dilate at night, to allow all possible light to enter. It is interesting to note that these hunters of the gloom have the largest eyes of all the carnivores.

CATS OLD AND NEW

Cats vary from medium to large in size. Although they are not native to the Australian region and Madagascar, we find them in most other parts of the world, particularly in its hotter regions. (However, they originated in the colder regions—hence the warm, thick fur.)

In prehistoric times, one of the commonest of the cats in Europe, Asia, Africa, and North and South America was the famous sabre-toothed tiger. About the size of a modern lion or tiger, it had enormous sabre-like teeth projecting from its upper jaw. Apparently, it preyed on animals with leathery hides, and could not have overcome them with a more modest armament.

It was a long step from this ancient warrior to today's domestic cat. The ancestors of our domestic cat were probably the African Wild Cat, *Felis chaus*, and the Kaffir Cat, *Felis lybica* (others no doubt are also in its family tree). These two were tamed by the Egyptians of olden times and ultimately brought to Europe. Here they were crossed with local species, and many of our modern cats sprang from the match.

Typical domestic cats usually have vertical black stripes on the flanks called "mackerel" by cat fanciers; but there are numerous curious and divergent breeds, among them the Manx cat, which lacks a tail; the Persian, which has long, silky hair; and the Siamese, whose hind legs are longer than the front ones.

Domestic cats have their cult, but their popularity today is only a pale shadow of the esteem they enjoyed among the ancient Egyptians, who were among the first to tame them. Cats were sacred to the goddess

Bast, who was herself cat-headed. In tomb paintings we sometimes see rather long-eared, ginger-coloured cats, with lengthy, dark-ringed tails, sitting on chairs; one cat is portrayed wearing a collar and chewing a bone. One interesting painting depicts a long-faced cat perched on a papyrus stem, and we are led to believe that the animal filled the role of a retriever on hunting expeditions.

Herodotus tells us that the death of a cat was an occasion of deepest mourning among the Egyptians. It was a common practice to embalm the felines and wrap them in mummy bandages. Great numbers were reverently laid to rest in sacred cat cemeteries at Bubastis, a city devoted to the worship of cats, and other places along the Nile. In some localities the quantities of cat bones dug up in recent times were so vast that they were spread on the land or shipped abroad as fertilizer.

Some Interesting Smaller Wild Cats

EUROPE'S WILD CAT

Once common in England, the European Wild Cat, *Felis silvestris*, has retreated as civilization has moved forward. Today this savage creature still may be seen in Scotland and across Central Europe into Asia Minor and northern Asia. It resembles a tabby cat in size and general colour (perhaps it is one of its ancestors) but is more heavily built and more powerful. The Scottish wild cat is about two feet long, with the tail half as long again.

The European wild cat chooses for its home rocky and densely wooded regions. Its den is hidden in a thicket or crevice in the rocks or under an old tree stump. A fierce, ill-tempered beast, it haunts the shores of lakes and rivers at night, searching for rabbits, grouse, mountain hares, small birds, and, occasionally, fish. It stalks its game by sight until within a short distance. Then the wild cat puts on tremendous speed, making the final attack as unexpected as possible.

This animal is quite untamable, and makes a most unsatisfactory pet. It never turns docile, even to those who feed it. Most other cats become amenable to discipline but the wild cat always has its back to the wall: with ears down and eyes glittering, it holds its paws forever ready to strike at the least provocation. Captive animals have lived as long as sixteen years.

THE JUNGLE CAT

One of the most familiar cats of India and North Africa is the Jungle Cat or African Wild Cat, *Felis chaus*. It ranges through southern Asia as far east as Thailand and Yunnan China. This feline haunts the brush jungles, tall grass, and reed beds near rivers and lakes but mostly in areas that are comparatively dry. The author found it common in the arid regions near the Caspian Sea in Persia and saw several asleep on dry mudbanks in broken country.

About the size of a large house cat, the jungle cat is coloured grey to tawny and has a distinct crest of hairs along its back. It has long legs and is very swift and strong for its size. Its food is mainly small mammals and birds up to the size of the peacock. The discovery of the quills of the porcupine in its feet indicates that it occasionally attacks this animal.

An African subspecies, known as the Egyptian Fettered Cat, or the Swamp Cat, was tamed by the ancient Egyptians, and mummified cats of this type are found in the Egyptian tombs.

THE KAFFIR CAT AND THE BLACK-FOOTED CAT

The Kaffir Cat, or Grey Wild Cat, *Felis lybica*, is the common wild cat of Africa, from Egypt to the Cape of Good Hope. It looks like a tabby cat, its fur being tawny or light buff in colour, as a rule.

The kaffir, like almost all the cats, keeps to itself, remaining under cover in dense brush or tall grass. It is, however, a hefty creature and can defend itself against almost any dog. When at bay, it erects the ruff around its neck and presents a most formidable appearance to its foes.

The smallest of the wild cats is the Black-footed Cat, or Sebala Cat, *Felis (Microfelis) nigripes*. It is only fourteen inches long, plus a six-inch tail. Native to the arid plains of the Kalahari Desert region and South Africa, it rests during the day in the hole of the springhaas or some other burrowing animal.

A shy creature, the black-footed cat usually remains savage in captivity, though it will live on amicable terms with other cats. It breeds readily with domestic cats and other small wild species of typical cats. The black-footed cat's litter, like that of many others in this group, contains two or three kittens.

LYNXES AND BOBCATS

The Canadian Lynx, *Felis* (*Lynx*) *canadensis*, dwells in the evergreen forests of the North Country of Canada, where fallen timber and dense windfalls present an almost impenetrable barrier to man.

A black-barred side-ruff and ears heavily tufted and edged with black frame this feline's solemn-eyed face and give it a handsome, almost regal appearance. But gaunt, lanky hind quarters, bobtail, and

"MR. SOBERSIDES"

Long side whiskers make the Canadian lynx look solemn and old-fashioned. Despite its name, it is also found in the United States, usually in northern evergreen forests. The animal's broad feet and strong legs enable it to tread the snowy terrain. Lynx fur—greyish brown with black spots—is in demand in the fur trade because of its long, soft, feather-light hair. Man takes a greater toll of the lynx than do any of its natural enemies.

exceptionally long hind legs and oversized feet are incongruous with the elegance of the animal's mien. Although the large, padded feet make the going across the snow easier, the lynx is an awkward animal when it speeds up to a gallop.

Despite its name, the Canadian lynx ranges as far south as Colorado

and Oregon in the west, northern New York in the east. It is much
sought by trappers and hunters for its long, soft fur, which is grizzled
or greyish brown in colour and spotted with black. The pelt is highly
valued in the fur trade, and is warm as well as handsome.

Famous for the sharpness of its sight, the lynx usually hunts at night.
It feeds largely on the snowshoe rabbit, and when the supply of these
animals fails, as happens from time to time, many of the cats die of
starvation. Sometimes the lynx ekes out its diet with beaver, and it is a
deadly enemy of the fox. It will prey on deer, but these swift, massive
animals are no easy quarry for the three-foot-long lynx. It prefers to
creep up on them while they are lying down, and then spring at the
neck, holding on till the victim is dead. The lynx can strike with
unbelievable swiftness at the crucial moment.

Oddly enough for a cat, the lynx is not averse to getting itself wet.
Those who have watched it say that it takes to the water without being
in any sense driven, and that it swims as well as a dog. One lynx was
seen crossing the arm of a lake two miles wide.

Family Life of the Lynx. During the mating season—in late winter
or early spring—there is considerable caterwauling as the tom lynxes
fight for a mate, but usually there is more sound than actual struggle.
About two months after mating time a litter of kittens—generally
four—is born in the shelter of a thick windfall or under an overhanging
ledge (typical lairs of the lynx). Blind at birth, they open their eyes
for the first time when ten days old. Their mother suckles them for two
or three months, when they are old enough to travel with her on her
hunting trips.

By midsummer the kittens are weaned, and begin the task of hunting
for themselves. The family stays together until the autumn, and may
continue together until the end of the year, by which time the
kittens are fully grown. But when the mating season rolls around
again, all family ties are broken and the young are ready to seek their
own mates.

Life in the wild is hard for the lynx. Although it does not have
many enemies, food is often scarce and the animal may have to risk
its life to get it. Under favourable circumstances it might live fifteen
years, but that would be a record.

The Not-So-Fearful Bobcats. Much like the Canadian lynx, but
smaller, is the Bay Lynx, Bobcat, or Wild Cat, *Lynx rufus* ("red lynx"),

as it is variously known. This creature has brown fur, indistinctly marked with darker spots and lines, but its feet are more normal than the Canadian lynx's. Its range is not so northerly, extending from southern Canada into Mexico. Varying from this animal in size and colour are many North American bobcats that all belong in the genus *Lynx* but dwell in restricted localities.

The bobcats have a reputation for ferocity that is more a matter of seeming than of reality. Their usual fare is rats, mice, rabbits, and snakes, and they are most unlikely to attack man. Sometimes they prey on small domestic stock and poultry.

Bobcat hunting is a popular sport in the south-eastern United States. The animal is not easy to tree; it will give a pack of fast foxhounds a good run for their money, sometimes eluding them for hours. When the bobcat can no longer escape, it strikes out ferociously at the dogs. Though they generally put it out of action, they have wounds to nurse and lick.

Most of the bobcats appear to have no fixed breeding season. The mother bears two to four babies at a time in her den, which may be in caves, dense shrubbery, or in a hollow log.

Quick Thinking of a Bobcat Mother. To a gentleman named Blennerhassett, who lived in West Virginia, we owe a fascinating picture of how a mother bobcat protects her young. While on a fishing trip in the mountains of that state, he saw a mother bobcat with her two kittens emerge from a clump of underbrush. The cat seemed to be giving her young a lesson, when suddenly she grabbed one of them by the loose skin of its neck and deposited it in the crotch of a tree near by. Leaving the startled youngster there, she darted back for the remaining one.

Just as the mother bobcat got her second baby up the tree, an old razorback boar dashed out of the brush, followed by a wild sow with a litter of little pigs. The cat had barely gone ten feet up when the boar was stamping with rage at the foot of the tree.

Leaving her kittens at a safe distance from the ground, the cat took her position lower down; now it seemed that she was going to fight the boar.

But the wise old cat had no such intentions. She waited and waited until the boar was at a safe distance. Then she sprang at one of the little pigs and made off with it as fast as her long legs could carry her. Over logs and rocks she raced, with the boar foaming at the mouth in hot pursuit.

The trail ended at a cliff. Here the cat dropped the pig and sprang to safety. Presently she returned to the tree, retrieved her kittens, and trotted off into the forest.

It would seem that this bobcat showed considerable forethought in her method of decoying the boar away from her little ones. Being a parent herself, she knew full well that the infuriated wild razorback could not ignore the pitiful cries of his young and would give chase, and that her own babies would be left safely behind.

Old World Lynxes. The Old World has its lynxes, too, though man, the hunter, has made them much scarcer than they used to be. The European Lynx, *Lynx lynx*, closely resembling the Canadian lynx, is found throughout the wooded portions of Europe, except Britain, and Asia from the extreme north to the Alps, the Pyrenees, and Tibet, and from the Atlantic coast east to the Pacific coast in Siberia. There are a number of regional lynxes that vary in colour from a Chinese variety that is reddish brown with dark spots, to yellowish brown or brownish grey in the typical European lynx.

CARACALS—OFTEN TRAINED FOR HUNTING

The Caracal, *Felis* (*Caracal*) *caracal*, is among the most active of the feline tribe. Except for the cheetah, it is the least catlike of all in its movements.

The natives of India often train this animal for hunting because of its remarkable speed and its skill in jumping. Trained caracals are let loose amongst pigeons feeding on the ground and one cat may strike down ten or twelve before they can escape by flight. The cat will spring five or six feet in the air to knock down a pigeon.

"Caracal" means "black ears" in Turkish, and this slender, lynx-like animal does indeed have large, blackish ears that are tufted at the tip. Its fur is rather short and tawny brown in colour. The tail is not long (nine inches) compared to the body (about two and one-half feet). The animal may weigh up to forty pounds and stands high on its long limbs. This handsome cat has eyes that shine like bright emeralds, due to the lustre of the enlarged pupils; the iris is an amber yellow.

The caracal is essentially a creature of hot, dry country. In Asia it is found over the greater part of Arabia, as well as in Turkey, Syria, Iraq, and the Peninsula of India. In Africa it ranges from the Mediterranean Sea to the Cape of Good Hope, in all types of country but the thick tropical coastal forests. Its den may be a hollow tree, a crevice in the rocks, or a hole in the ground (a porcupine or aardvark burrow), and here it bears its two to five young. The caracal preys on peacocks, cranes, partridges, hares, and occasionally gazelles.

OCELOTS—FAMED FOR THEIR FUR

The Ocelot, *Felis* (*Leopardus*) *pardalis*, is an American jungle cat that loves darkness. At home in the gloom of dense forests, it never leaves its lair until the evening light is gone and the dusk has turned to darkness. The darker the night the farther the ocelot will prowl. Even moonlit nights impede its activities.

Usually the ocelot spends its time on the ground, in dense cover on brush-laden hillsides. But it is also fond of climbing in the trees: it often goes aloft to rifle bird nests and may even sleep in trees during daylight hours. That it can find its prey in the branches of the dark forest is a tribute to its keen senses. It can climb easily and quickly enough for its own purpose, though it is not in the same class as the squirrels and monkeys.

This long, lithe animal will seek refuge up a tree when danger threatens. However, it does not leave the ground at the first yap of a pack of hounds. It can run like a fox and knows how to backtrack and double-cross its trail.

The ocelot feeds on almost any kind of animal life that it can master, including—besides birds—rodents, snakes, lizards, and opossums. On one occasion an ocelot killed a large boa, six or seven feet long, and, when discovered, had eaten the head and neck. An ocelot will consume from three to five pounds of meat a night.

For its den the ocelot nearly always selects a rocky cave or, failing this, a hollow tree. The home, wherever it is, is lined with great care. The animal chooses bedding of dry grass, twigs, and the like, and chews it till it is soft and pliable, for this creature likes its comfort.

The mating season is probably about June. The kittens, nearly always twins, are born in September or October, with their eyes tightly closed. When taken young enough, an ocelot can be tamed, but the less tractable temper and large size of the full-grown adult make it somewhat undesirable for a house pet.

Perhaps the ocelot is most familiar to us through the use of its fur on women's coats and collars. It is one of the handsomest of the cats. Its basic colour is light buff, with a pearly overtone. Longitudinal black stripes score its face, head, and neck; there are black spots splashed across the limbs and tail, and dots and black rings cover the rest of the body in an attractive, rather chainlike pattern. From the tip of its nose to the end of its tail the animal is three or four feet long.

THE OCELOT WEARS AN ATTRACTIVE COAT

One of the brightest furs used to decorate women's coats is that of the ocelot, a wild cat of South America and Mexico. Against a light buff background, an interesting medley of black rings, spots, and stripes makes a striking contrast. The hair of the ocelot is soft and short. This animal is a fierce fighter, and has even been known to kill boas.

The range of the ocelot extends from the south-western United States down to Paraguay. The animal is now scarce north of the Rio Grande, but farther south it is quite common.

MORE ABOUT THE LESSER CATS

The Cat With Long Legs. Every kind of cat lives in its own chosen field; each of these springers has characteristics best suited for a particular kind of life and surroundings. The Serval, *Felis (Leptailurus) serval*, a beautiful thirty-four-pound golden buff-coloured cat, marked profusely with bold black spots, is found over most of Africa south of the Sahara. Its long legs are a superb adaptation for an animal that lives by running on the ground. This creature haunts the reed-fringed lakes and rivers where waterfowl and hares are to be had. There are two distinct species, the Large Spotted Serval and the Small Spotted Serval.

The Cat That Eats Fruit. All animals live to eat or to be eaten. We generally look upon cats as hunters and flesh-eaters, and correctly so, but there are exceptions; the Flat-headed Cat, *Felis (Ictailurus) planiceps*, smallest of the wild cats in tropical eastern Asia, actually prefers eating nice juicy fruit to catching rats and mice. (Lions often devour ripe water-melons on the Kalahari Desert, but this they seem to do more to obtain liquid than to satisfy their appetites.)

The Cat That Goes Fishing. A cat may wash its face with its paws and make a good job of it, but cats in general just do not like water; most resent getting even their feet wet. A bath is unheard of in the cat family. Yet we find that there is a cat that haunts the banks of rivers and streams in the tropical regions of India and east to Malaya.

This animal, the Fishing Cat, *Felis (fzibethailurus) viverrina*, has turned from the hereditary feline practice of hunting and has gone a-fishing. Having a cat's dislike of getting wet, it does not enter the water. Instead, it crouches on overhanging banks and with a sweep of its paw scoops up fish as they sail unsuspectingly by.

Fresh-water molluscs are also eaten by this short-limbed, sturdy, spotted cat (it is about two and one-half feet long). It will resort to killing animals and birds where fishing does not fill its needs, and has been known to carry off dogs and even small children.

The Marbled Cat. The superb long tail of the Marbled Cat, *Felis (Pardofelis) marmorata*, tells us that this handsome creature lives in tall trees; the large irregularly spaced dark blotches that mark its coat are indiscernible against the living tracery of dark forests. The

Lewis Wayne Walker—National Audubon Society

AN INDIAN MONGOOSE SURPRISED WITH HIS PREY

The mongoose is one of the commonest flesh-eaters of Africa, southern Asia, and the Pacific islands. A long-tailed, weasel-like animal, it preys extensively upon rodents, but is most noted for its talent as a destroyer of poisonous snakes. Mongooses are generally not immune to venom; they depend upon their very sharp vision and agility to avoid a fatal snakebite.

Freelance Photographers Guild

TREACHEROUS PREDATOR OR DOCILE, EFFICIENT RETRIEVER?

This leopard, raised in captivity, is the latter. Ranking high in intelligence, leopards are quick to learn and easily remember anything that is to their advantage. Smaller and more common than the lion or tiger the leopard is considered to surpass both in sheer malevolence and savagery, and throughout its wide range in Africa and Asia the wily, wary trickster is generally more feared than either. See page 576.

marbled cat travels the dense jungles from the Himalayas east to Borneo, where it becomes a mahogany red and is known as the Bay Cat.

The Golden Cat. Among the rock-bound wastes of south-eastern Asia, from Tibet to Malaya, lives one of the largest and most attractive of the medium-sized cats, the Golden Cat, *Felis (Profelis) temminckii*. The bright reddish-brown coat of this creature blends perfectly with the rocky background of its home. It is an important animal to the Chinese, who call it *huang pao*—"yellow leopard"—and pay a high price for its bones in medicine shops. A related species of golden cat ranges the forests of West Africa.

The Chinese Money Cat. There is an animal that goes by the intriguing popular name of the Chinese Money Cat. To scientists it is better known as the Asiatic Leopard Cat, *Felis (Prionailurus) bengalensis*. This feline's mercenary name comes from its many spots, which resemble Chinese money—a kind of decoration that makes ideal camouflage for a forest-loving animal.

The Rusty Spotted Cat. In the broken bush country of southern India and western Ghats is the home of the Rusty Spotted Cat, *Felis rubiginosus*. Its rust-coloured spots are arranged in rows or stripes that make this cat almost invisible as it steals silently through the fields of tall grass.

The Desert Cat. At night on the great deserts of western India that stretch westward to northern Africa, the gerbils and numerous other rodents are out to feast on the few blades of grass and seeds that are thinly scattered over the sandy wastes. Here the Desert Cat, *Felis constantina*, a house-cat-sized species with pale sandy-coloured fur, marked with numerous small black spots, keeps their number in check.

The Rock-Dweller. The Manul or Pallas Cat, *Felis (Otocolobus) manul*, is a small spotted cat that dwells in the high mountains of Tibet and northward into Siberia. Its eyes, placed high in the face, and the low-set ears give it a most ferocious appearance. So far as we may gather, the position of the eyes is an adaptation for peering over edges of rocks in search of prey, thus exposing the smallest amount of the head possible

SOME INTERESTING SOUTH AMERICAN CATS

The Cat like a Weasel. Perhaps the strangest of all the cat family is the Yaguarundi or Eyra, *Felis (Herpailurus) eyra*. This short-legged, long-bodied cat with a lengthy tail resembles a weasel more than it does a cat and fills much the same position in tropical America that the weasel cats do in the Old World. In Mexico it is known as the Otter Cat in tribute to its readiness to take to the water.

The yaguarundi is only two feet long but it is a ferocious, untamable creature. Its home is in the tangled thickets and dense brush of the plains as well as the forested country from Texas south to Argentina. It is one of the few species that come in two distinct colour phases (that is, it may have a coat of one or the other of two colours): one a speckled grey or black and the other a bright rusty red.

Stripes and Spots Galore. The Andean Highland Cat, *Felis (Oreailurus) jacobita*, of South America, takes the place of the snow leopard in the New World; it is pale grey in colour and more or less marked with the ocelot's stripes. It is a big cat, too, nearly three feet long without its lengthy tail.

On the upland grass plains that stretch from Patagonia to northern Argentina is the Pampas Cat, *Felis (Dendrailurus) pajeros*, a large yellowish cat with rather coarse fur. In the extreme southern part of South America there is Geoffroy's Spotted Cat, *Felis (Oncifelis)geoffroyi*, while the Margay, *Felis (Noctifelis) wiedii*, a much smaller cat liberally marked with black stripes and spots, lives in the forests of Paraguay and north to Texas. A cat with small spots—the Tiger Cat, *Felis pardinoides*—is the smallest of the American wild cats. It haunts the forests from Costa Rica to Chile.

The Big Cats

COUGARS—POWERFUL VOICES AND BODIES

THE COUGAR, *Felis (Puma) concolor*, is a fear-inspiring sight to the traveller who glimpses this great, powerful beast crouching in the branches of a tree in a deep forest. Its eyes seem to glow like fire in its small, round head. The lithe six-foot body, covered with short, tawny or greyish-brown fur, and the long, heavy tail are vibrant with deadly energy. Those who have heard this feline's weird drawn-out shriek declare it to be the wildest and most hair-raising sound that ever broke the stillness of the American wilderness.

The cougar is a big-game hunter. Usually it spends the day sleeping in some rocky cavern or sunning itself on a high, warm ledge. After dark the cougar leaves its lair and sets forth on a silent hunt. More than once it has been seen swimming across rivers at least a mile wide. It may range twenty miles through the night.

This big cat's natural prey are the deer and sometimes the elk, but it will track down other animals like the skunk, and its victims often include domestic stock—cattle, sheep, horses, and pigs. Stalking the doomed animal in the shadows, the cougar approaches soundlessly for the final rush. Now it gathers its feet under its body and humps its back. The taut muscles burst into action. In one, two, or three quick bounds, the cougar is upon its quarry, hurling it to the ground and piercing its throat or neck with long, murderous fangs.

The cougar is no mean jumper; it can spring twenty feet in one leap. It has no fear of dropping from a height, and has been known to jump from a perch sixty feet high without doing itself injury.

This animal, we see, has enormous power concealed in its graceful body. It can drag a victim that weighs five times its own 160 pounds for a good one hundred yards. If the kill is large, the cougar will eat

573

its fill, then cover the remnants with brush. Later it will come back and make a second or a third meal of the carcass.

Except for the jaguar, the cougar is the largest of the New World cats. The two are almost irreconcilable foes and when they meet there is the devil to pay. The jaguar is bigger and more powerful, but it cannot match the cougar's remarkable agility. The odds are naturally in the jaguar's favour, yet frequently it loses the bout.

NOT A MAN-KILLER

Ferocious the cougar certainly is, but not when it comes up against man. Authentic accounts of attacks upon human beings by this big cat are scarce. It evinces considerable curiosity about people and their actions and will prowl about an abandoned camp or dwelling. But let somebody appear on the scene and the cougar moves off into the woods.

Because of the damage it does to domestic stock, this big cat is extensively hunted. The hunters use dogs to corner the cougar. When it sees no other way out, the animal takes to a tree. Such a move is

IT COMES TO SPY UPON MAN, NOT TO KILL HIM

Anyone who has ever heard the blood-curdling shriek of the cougar, or puma, or seen its powerful, menacing body poised on a tree branch, has surely turned in terror. Yet the otherwise savage cougar does not attack man; it is merely curious about him and likes to poke around his habitations. The cougar's victims are game and domestic animals; its appetite for sheep and cattle causes farmers severe losses.

likely to be fatal for the cougar; a well-placed shot will quickly finish the hunt.

A TAME COUGAR

Now and then you will hear of people rearing tame cougars. Some years ago, in Utah, the author made the acquaintance of a forester who kept as a house pet a cougar that he had raised from a kitten. The big cat was exceedingly playful, and whenever the ranger returned home in the evening, the cougar would make a pretence of hiding behind a chair. Naturally the man was well aware of what was going on, since the chair would hardly conceal the great bulk of the animal. But, entering into the spirit of the game, he would sit down and open his evening paper. With one bound the huge cat would leap over the paper, land on the forester's shoulder, and nuzzle his head and neck in a friendly, loving manner.

Eventually the animal had to go; it had ripped the rugs to pieces and scratched the paint off the walls in sharpening its claws. Transferred to a zoo, the cougar became more and more irritable and savage and would not let the keepers near it.

SEQUEL

Two years later the forester visited the zoo. Despite the keepers' insistent warnings, the man walked to the cage, opened the door, and walked in. To the amazement of all the watchers, the cougar jumped on to the forester's shoulder, nearly knocking him over, and nuzzled his neck and face. The cat had not forgotten its friend.

COUGAR KITTENS

The mating season of the cougar is very irregular; this cat breeds at almost any time of the year. About three kittens are born some ninety days after a brief courtship.

At birth, a kitten measures about twelve inches and weighs one pound; it is blind and covered with fine yellowish fur spotted with black. The kitten opens its eyes on the eighth or ninth day and cuts its first teeth about ten days later. The spots usually fade from the fur when the animal is six months of age. The kittens stay with their mother until they are a year or sometimes two years old. A long life among the cougars is twenty years.

COUGARS TODAY AND YESTERDAY

There are twenty-seven subspecies of the cougar known. It goes under various names—Puma, Panther, Painter, Catamount, and Mountain Lion—and was once very abundant in the Americas from southern Canada to Patagonia. Today its range in the United States has shrunk to the more remote wilderness of Florida, Louisiana, and the western states from British Columbia to Mexico.

The cougar is still fairly well represented in Central America and South America, where it was a popular game animal long before the coming of the white man. The Inca rulers and their Indian subjects had spectacular hunting excursions, in which the big cat figured prominently. As many as thirty thousand drivers took part in these round-ups, destroying great numbers of cougars and other predatory animals.

In Baja California, on the other hand, the natives depended on the cougar for food in quite another way. The hungry Indians, we are told, watched for the gathering of the buzzards and carefully searched the ground where these scavengers were. Often they would find the remains of a cougar feast which the lordly cat had left, in true feline fashion, hidden away beneath soil and leaves. There was often a sizable joint to be had.

LEOPARDS OR PANTHERS—FIERCE AND TREACHEROUS

The Leopard, Panther, or Golden Cash Leopard, *Panthera pardus*, outstrips both the lion and the tiger in pure malevolence and savagery. The smallest of the three, this cat is barely inferior to its two big cousins in fighting ability. The natives of Africa often say they would rather face a lion than a leopard any time.

This wary, treacherous beast is much more given to climbing and lurking in the trees than either the lion or tiger. It can leap more than ten feet in the air and run up the side of a tree with astonishing speed. Sometimes it drags its prey up into the branches with it, so that it can dine in peace, away from other marauders.

Although the leopard may be about in the daytime, it is most active in the darkness. A clever tracker, a patient waiter in ambush, it preys on domestic cattle and sheep, deer, antelope, monkeys, and small wild life. It knows better than to attack a pack of baboons, for these can defend themselves; a single baboon, however, might not be so fortunate.

The panther will spring after its quarry, overtaking it in a few long leaps. It can subdue its smaller victims in a few instants by breaking their spines, strangling them, or tearing open their throats.

INTELLIGENCE OF THE LEOPARD

In intelligence the leopard ranks high; it is quick to learn, and retains anything that is to its advantage. One thing it learns early is ruse, and it occasionally resorts to the subtlest and wiliest subterfuge to make a kill.

THE LEOPARD—A DECEITFUL FIGHTER

Savage and wily, the leopard, or panther, is especially dangerous because its fondness for dog's flesh may bring it close to human dwellings. Leopards sometimes turn into notorious man-eaters, cleverly eluding capture for long, bloody years. Not generally known is the fact that the leopard isn't always clearly spotted—the black panther is also a leopard. Some leopards raised in captivity may grow up to be quite docile.

With a deer in the neighbourhood, the leopard has been observed to roll on the ground and to indulge in various other playful antics. The deer, its curiosity aroused, moves closer, but remains suspicious. Still the cat carries on, and the deer, in wonderment, draws nearer in order to see better. Those last few steps are the ones the trickster has been waiting for—they bring the intended victim within easy striking distance.

A FEARLESS ANIMAL

The domestic dog is one of the leopard's favourite foods. At Lihnshan, a small village in China, a very bold leopard entered the open window of a house, went straight to the bed where the owner was sleeping, and made off with a dog that was tied there. The next night it returned and carried away another dog from the room.

It seems that man is less likely to change his ways than is a leopard. The following night the man tethered another dog to his bed; this night the leopard did not show up, but on the next it did and, though a watch was kept, it escaped with its victim into the forest. A few days later it carried off a pig from a village only a few miles away.

Eventually the leopard was tracked down and killed, but not before it had wounded three people.

Normally, a leopard will not attack a man. If provoked or wounded, however, the animal will turn on human beings and fight. Once in a great while a leopard will become a man-killer, and take many lives in a short span of time.

WHERE WE FIND THEM

In the warmer and some of the colder parts of the Old World, the leopard is far commoner than the lion or the tiger. It ranges from the Black Sea in Europe east to Burma and the Malay Peninsula, including the whole of India and Ceylon, and north into Amurland, Siberia. In Africa it is found almost everywhere except in the Sahara.

DIFFERENT KINDS OF LEOPARDS

Leopards vary greatly in size. Some are as long as nine feet, including the extensive tail; others are seven feet in total length or smaller. Their average weight is about one hundred pounds. Twenty years is as long as a leopard is likely to live. It bears two to five young in a litter.

Originally people believed that the leopard and the panther were two different animals. However, the difference proved to be only one of size or sex: the male, the larger of the species, was the so-called "panther" and the female the "leopard".

The entire body of a typical leopard is profusely covered with large and small black spots, evenly scattered over the pale yellowish-buff fur. The spots are arranged in groups of four or five in a circle, or rosette, about a centre of somewhat darker shade than the main body colour. But we find many variations among the leopards, the most striking being a jet-coloured creature known as the Black Panther, which is fairly common in Ethiopia and the East Indies.

THE LEOPARD'S COAT

The kind of coat a leopard wears will depend very much upon the climate of its native land. Leopards in hot countries have short, close fur, while, in the colder regions, especially Siberia, the hair is long, thick, soft, and deep.

It is in Siberia that we meet the handsomest of all these cats, the Siberian Leopard, a magnificent creature with bluish-grey eyes and long-haired spotted fur almost pearl grey in colour. Its agreeable appearance is matched by a pleasant disposition, and in captivity this cat is the most amiable and tractable of its species.

"FALSE LEOPARDS"

The Clouded Leopard. Two of the most attractive of all the cats are called leopards, but are not leopards at all. One of these is the Clouded Leopard, *Panthera* (*Neofelis*) *nebulosa*, of south-eastern Asia. It has thick, soft, and full fur, beautifully decorated with spots and stripes. A savage and extremely wary creature, it inhabits the densest of forests and is active only at night, so that it is rarely seen.

Although only about three feet long, this beast is powerfully built and has relatively longer canine teeth than other cats, so that it is capable of killing fair-sized game, including deer, though generally it preys on smaller mammals and birds.

The clouded leopard is not apt to attack man unprovoked, but there is an instance where a clouded leopard that had killed several head of cattle started to stalk a native boy; fortunately the boy was able to split the skull of the spotted greyish-brown cat with his knife.

In captivity, the clouded leopard often becomes quite tame and lets itself be handled.

The Snow Leopard. The other "leopard" that is not a leopard is known by various names: Snow Leopard, Ounce, or Irbis, *Panthera* (*Uncia*) *uncia*. It is often looked for by men who brave the cold, high altitudes from the Himalayas north to the Altai Mountains, where it dwells. Its superb coat of deep, soft fur, pale grey or creamy buff, ornamented with large rosettes, or broken black rings, is a grand reward for the efforts of any hunter.

NOT A TRUE LEOPARD, THOUGH IT HAS THE LEOPARD'S SPOTS

Erroneously named a "leopard", probably because it is spotted with the familiar black rings or rosettes, the snow leopard or ounce has a beautiful coat of pale grey or buff. This beast lives high above the timber line of the Himalayas and, like many animals that dwell in cold places, has a soft, long-haired pelt.

The snow leopard is about the size of an average leopard but less powerful. It preys on mountain sheep, goats, hares, and other small game.

LIONS—THE SOCIABLE BIG CATS

The Lion, or Simba, *Panthera* (*Leo*) *leo*, has for a long time been known as the King of Beasts. It certainly looks the part: it has size, a dignified and noble face, and what would seem great pride. Then, of course, it wears a long, stately mane around its neck, which adds to the beast's air of majesty.

But if the lion is a king, it is not one by virtue of savagery. On the contrary, this animal usually has a friendly nature. All other cats travel alone or in pairs; the lion is the only one that moves about in a group or "pride". Occasionally you may see a lion by itself, but these creatures love company, and more often there are five or six together.

The lions will not fight over prey. As many as six male lions have been observed feeding on one kill, and other than a resentful growl when two got hold of the same chunk of meat, there was no display of ill-feeling. At one time, on the Serengeti Plains of East Africa, the author had twenty-five lions, including lionesses and cubs, feeding around him, some not ten feet away. They all got up and left peacefully, without haste, when he stood up.

The lion favours open broken country and grassy plains rather than dense tropical forests. In southern Asia today it is a rarity, but it is still found throughout most of Africa south of the Sahara Desert, being more or less plentiful where there is an abundance of big game. During the day lions often lie up in clumps of tall elephant grass or tangled brush. On the open veldt they are seen resting without any cover in broad daylight, for the royal family of the carnivores has few natural enemies to fear.

HOW THE LIONS KILL

Although these great beasts may be active by day, their working hours are chiefly at night. The lion hunts the larger game such as water-buck, wildebeest, and kudu, but it seems to prefer the zebra.

Frequently, the big cat lies in wait for its prey near waterholes and grazing grounds. In attacking, the lion creeps stealthily on its quarry, coming up from the side or rear. Its head down and its tail erect, it utters low growls. It may be one hundred feet off when it breaks into the final rush, and it dashes toward its prey at a speed of about forty miles per hour or more.

In its attack on a zebra, an experienced lion will gallop alongside the animal and slap it on the neck with its mighty paw. Then the king of beasts slows down and waits for the zebra to fall. The lion's blow may not cut the skin, but it is delivered with such accuracy that it will dislocate the zebra's neck. More often, the lion sinks its teeth into the neck of its prey. With one paw hooked on to the victim's shoulder, it reaches with the other around the animal's head and twists it back, throwing the zebra to the ground and breaking its neck.

WHY HE KILLS

Not nearly so bloodthirsty as some of the other big cats, the lion never destroys other animals for the fun of it. A lion kills to live: it kills only when it must eat, and then only one animal at a time. A single carcass will satisfy a lion's hunger for several days.

Normally when a lion has brought down a victim, it feeds on the spot. Afterward it sits close by to guard the carcass from thieves. In a nearby tree, vultures will settle and wait patiently for the lion to leave. But the lion remains until it has made a number of meals off the kill. Then the vultures and the hyenas close in.

MAN-EATING LIONS

We have seen that lions respect man. As a rule, they are more apt to run than attack when met on the veldt, unless provoked or hunted. Still, now and then, you will hear of a man-eater. The percentage of lions that turn man-killer is low. Lions that prey on human beings are usually (but not always) older individuals that have become incapable of killing wild game for themselves. They make their attack only under cover of darkness, and then drag their victim away and hide in the bush.

Two man-eating lions have won a place in history: they actually held up the construction of the Uganda Railway in East Africa. Time and again they returned and carried off and devoured men working on the railroad. Apparently these beasts—they were both males—had a close bond of friendship, as lions occasionally will.

The engineer in charge, a Mr. Patterson, said that, in advancing to the attack on the railway camps, the lions would roar loudly to one another. But they were always absolutely silent during the hour preceding the actual seizure of their unfortunate victims, so it was hard to tell exactly where they would attack. Ultimately Mr. Patterson succeeded in shooting them (December, 1898) but not before they had killed and eaten twenty-eight Indian coolies as well as scores of African natives.

Another lion, after killing several men around a station on the railway, even managed to carry off and eat the superintendent of the division. This gentleman had come down in his private car, which was run in on a siding. He sat up at a window that night, gun in hand, to watch for the lion, but after a while he fell asleep. The lion climbed on the platform, entered the car, and made off with its would-be slayer.

The man-eating lion, rare though it is, presents a serious menace. If it has killed once, it is likely to kill again; the taste for human flesh, once acquired, is usually retained for life. Thus, in Africa, the killing of a human being by a lion is the signal for organizing an extensive hunt. With modern weapons, the animal is quickly exterminated, though not without considerable risk to the hunter.

TRAINED LIONS

In circuses, lions are closely watched. Because they are highly intelligent, quick to learn, and friendly, it is simple to teach them tricks and get them to obey commands. The trainer's axiom, however, is: "Easily trained but never tamed."

Lions do occasionally kill their trainers. Nearly always, though, such unfortunate incidents appear to be the trainer's fault—he displays nervousness or changes his routine slightly, and the big cat gets upset. A lion can break a man's back with one blow of its heavy paw.

THE LION'S HONEYMOON

The docile part of a lion's nature, we perceive, is not uppermost all the time. In the breeding season this carnivore will even turn on its own kind. A lion must fight for a mate and it will engage its competitors in a fierce battle. Sometimes the beast has to defeat three or four rivals before it can claim its favourite lioness.

Once victory is won, the pair go off together on their honeymoon. They may travel for miles until they find a place that offers them suitable privacy. During the honeymoon, which may last two weeks or more, they do little hunting or eating. At this time the lion is really dangerous, and any man or beast that trespasses on its privacy is quickly annihilated.

In East Africa the author once saw a lion and a lioness alone together at the edge of the bush. The guide took one look at the couple and hustled the author off in the opposite direction. There could be no mistaking the lion's objection to intruders. The animal's ears were pulled firmly down, the tip of the tail was lashing back and forth, and there was a ferocious snarl on the lips, which were drawn tightly back, exposing a formidable array of teeth.

The lion is often said to take a single mate. So far as we know, its state of wedded bliss may last a year or longer. The animals definitely do not mate for life, and some males are polygamous.

LION CUBS

The lions have a variable breeding season. About 108 days after the mating, four cubs (the average number in a litter—though six are not unusual) are born. They are striped and thickly spotted, but their markings fade as the animals mature. Some, it has been said, have their eyes open at birth, but usually they are closed until the sixth day. In size the newborn babies resemble adult house cats.

The cubs are nursed until they are three months of age. Teething is a painful experience, and they may die in the process if separated from the parents. The cubs are not able to kill for themselves until they are a year old (at this time they are big enough to be on their own), and the mane does not begin to show until the male is three. Often the lion will supply the lioness with food while she is nursing newborn cubs, and will subsequently bring game to feed the growing family.

When half-grown, the whelps are expert climbers. They lose this skill as they grow older and heavier. Occasionally one may see a full-grown lion climb into the lower branches of a tree, but this is unusual.

When five or six years of age, a lion is in its prime. The average lion has a life span of fifteen years, but a long-lived one may reach the age of twenty-five.

MALE AND FEMALE

Lions are big fellows. A large male may weigh five hundred pounds and stand about three feet or more at the shoulder; such a beast measures seven feet in length, exclusive of its three-foot tail. The lioness, smaller and less powerful than her mate, will weigh up to three hundred pounds.

The coat of a lion is short haired and coarse, and uniformly tawny or pale sandy-brown in colour. The tip of the tail is tufted with dark-brown or black hairs, and completely hidden in it is the so-called "spur" or "claw", a naked, horny patch of skin. What purpose, if any, is served by the spur we do not know.

THE KING OF THE BEASTS IS A GOOD "FAMILY MAN"

The lion leads a surprisingly domestic existence. Generally travelling in family parties, it hunts for antelopes or zebras, and will amiably share the kill with its fellows. Exceptions to the lion's peacefulness occur during the breeding season, when the male will take his hard-won mate off for a secluded honeymoon, and deal swift, violent punishment to intruders. Normally lions will not attack man unless they have been provoked.

A lioness almost never has a mane. In the males, this growth of long hair is quite variable. Most wild lions possess only a scant, ragged, and straggly shock of hair. In menageries, particularly in northern climates, they are more likely to show the full, luxuriant ruff we commonly associate with them.

Although the lion is famous for its roar, the sound is almost never heard during daylight hours. But every evening after sunset, and throughout the night, the big cat periodically utters its ferocious-sounding grunts. "Uuummph-uuupf-mmmff" comes close to recording a typical, less forceful roar in words—if you want to give a realistic imitation, try producing these sounds from deep down in your throat.

HOME OF THE LIONS

Africa is the continent that has most of the world's lions, but even there they are not nearly so common as they used to be. They have disappeared from the extreme north and south. India also was once much more thickly populated with these great cats, which ranged from Sind in the north-west to Bengal in the north-east; but by 1880 the species was almost wholly exterminated except in the Gujarat region, where it still manages to hang on in the wilderness of the Gir forests.

You may well raise a sceptical eyebrow when you see lions and tigers grouped together in a motion-picture scene. There are no tigers in Africa, and lions are seldom seen in India. They are reported to have lingered on in Turkey, Iraq, and Iran until just before our day, but they long ago disappeared from Greece, Asia Minor, and Syria, where they were not uncommon in historic times. These big cats were well known to the Hebrew people, and there are few books of the Bible, either in the Old Testament or the New, that do not contain some mention of them. The strength of the lion is an often-repeated Scriptural reference.

An African lion was the first foreign wild animal to be exhibited in the United States.

The appearance of the animal in that country was officially announced in the *Boston Gazette* of 26 September, 1720. It must have been a profoundly exciting sight for the people of that day, for zoos did not become common in the New World until much later. When the Emperor of Morocco presented a lion to President Andrew Jackson, he was somewhat embarrassed by the gift, and asked Congress what to do with it. Following their advice, it was sold at auction and the proceeds were given to local orphanages. More recent Presidents have been able to solve such problems by turning them over to zoo curators.

Gregor—Monkmeyer Photo

HIS FATHER IS A LION, HIS MOTHER A TIGER

This young animal, known as a liger, is one of the great rarities of the animal kingdom. Such a hybrid generally has stripes, and may grow a mane when it is mature. The lion is the typical big cat of Africa; only a scant number of lions are found in Asia, home of the tiger, so that the two big cats seldom meet and never interbreed in Nature. *See page 587.*

A FUR SEAL FAMILY ENJOYING THE OCEAN BREEZES

The Alaska fur seals spend their summer on the Pribilof Islands of the North Pacific, where they mate and bear their babies. The sizable bull at the rear of this group watches jealously over his harem of six females and their young. More aggressive, powerful males may have a harem over ten times as large as this one and often fight savage battles to preserve it.

See page 601.

TIGERS—ASIA'S BIGGEST CATS

The Tiger, *Panthera (Tigris) tigris*, outdoes the lion in acts of brutal savagery and feats of power. Or that, in any event, is the conviction of men who have hunted or trained these two beasts. Still, both are almost of a size, and the tiger more nearly resembles the lion than any other member of the cat family.

The most striking differences between the two animals are the striped coat the tiger wears, and its lack of a mane. An old tiger will grow a rich ruff of long hair on its cheeks, but never a mane. Never, that is, unless it is half a lion. So closely related are the lion and the tiger that they may crossbreed in captivity.

You may have seen the interesting offspring of such a match in a zoo: the cross usually has stripes and will sometimes, when it reaches adulthood, sport a mane. A cross between a male lion and a female tiger is known as a liger; vice versa, it is a tigon (or tiglon). These hybrids are not common, however, for the tiger will rarely breed in captivity.

The tiger is the typical big cat of Asia. It lives as far north as Amurland, in Siberia, as far south as India and the Malay Peninsula. It is not native to Africa, and the closest it gets to Europe is the Caucasus, where people still report encountering it from time to time in the Elburz Mountains south of the Caspian Sea. Thus it is quite correct to picture the tiger as a giant cat slinking through the bush and the tangled growths of the steaming tropics—but remember that not all tigers will conform to this image. In its snow-covered winter homeland the Siberian Tiger must face temperatures that fall to seventy degrees below zero.

A CLIMBER AND A SWIMMER

A born climber, the tiger is a creature of the forests, preferring dense underbrush to big timber. Here its stripes seem to serve it as camouflage, blending in with the alternating dark and light of the woodland. The stripes also harmonize neatly with the dark and the dry grass on which the tiger rests. Crouching in the shade of the foliage, where it seeks to avoid the heat of the tropical day, the animal is not easy to detect. It favours places where there is good cover, and where it may find water without travelling far.

The more things an animal can do, the better is it equipped to survive. To its considerable advantage, the tiger is one of the cats that

can swim. (So can the lion, the lynx, and a few others.) It shows no
qualms about leaping into a stream. If it observes prey on the other
bank or on an island in midstream, it will swim across at a good rate.
With hunters at its heels, it often saves its life by taking to the water.
The animal is an extraordinarily good jumper, too—it can cover fifteen
feet in a single bound.

TIGER KITTENS

The tiger has no fixed mating season. The young—two to four make
up the average birth—come into the world about one hundred days
after the courtship. Newly born, the kittens weigh some two or three
pounds, and their eyes are sightless; the little cats cannot see before
they are two weeks old. A thoroughly devoted parent, their mother
watches over them with great tenderness, nursing them on her milk
until they are capable of devouring meat. Anyone who tries to take
her kittens from her will have to fight for his life. What role the father
plays is not clearly known.

When the kittens are about six weeks old, they may begin to travel
with the mother as she goes about her duties as flesh-winner for the
family. On hunts or at rest, they pass a sportive kittenhood, playing
and chasing their tails like cats the world over.

But by the time they have reached the age of six months or so, the
little cats must look to putting aside kittenish ways; now they are big
enough and strong enough to apply the tiger techniques of hunting
they have learned from their parent. The kittens start with smaller
game, like young pigs, and become increasingly adept at springing
upon their prey from ambush and slaying it with a quick bite in the
neck. They are a year old before they are able to shift for themselves.
Although tigers are not social at other times, the family may stay
together until the young are nearly two years old.

GETTING OLD

Tigers slow down as they get on in years, and they do not kill so
readily. Their teeth wear down and their power diminishes in time;
they must learn to content themselves with less. But a young tiger is
supercharged with vitality; it appears to take a special delight in killing
and at times exhibits a nature that is extremely bloodthirsty. If the
occasion presents itself, the animal will slay as many victims as it

finds available, without regard for its needs. And those needs are not small, as witnessed by the fact that a zoo tiger requires ten pounds of meat each day merely to keep its great body pacing back and forth in confinement.

TIGERS ON THE PROWL

For many generations tigers have bedevilled the poor farmer folk of India. In that traditionally hungry land, all it takes to undo a village is the presence of a tiger in the neighbouring woods. Under cover of darkness, the animal will steal forth and kill and carry off a treasured sheep, cow, or calf. If the carcass is of good size, the tiger may not be heard of again for several days; it rests in some hidden place, and dines repeatedly on the kill.

THE KILLER CAT

Just as powerful as the lion, the tiger is, by contrast, cruel, bloodthirsty, and solitary. It climbs, jumps, and, unlike most cats, even swims excellently. In India, the Bengal tiger alone has killed sixty thousand sheep, cows, and goats in one year. But, on the little-known credit side, the tiger helps to maintain a balance in Nature by preying upon deer and wild pigs, common despoilers of plant life.

But when nothing remains of the kill, hunger drives the great beast forth, and the village suffers another loss. This may go on for some time, since the peasants regard the tiger with superstitious dread, and are often slow to take action against it. In a single year the Bengal tiger is reported to have killed sixty thousand sheep, horses, and other livestock.

Tigers also prey upon deer, antelope, and wild pigs, but in such instances the big cats actually do man a service, since these vegetable-eaters often cause serious damage to crops.

TIGERS WITH A TASTE FOR HUMAN FLESH

Although tigers are not man-killers by nature, now and then they, like lions, acquire a taste for human flesh. This is especially true of tigers that are old, infirm, or crippled. Lacking the strength to cope with their natural prey—some intended victims, like the buffalo, have powerful horns, and are quite capable of killing the big cats—these older animals may discover that man is a helpless creature, relatively speaking.

When once a tiger takes to killing man, it usually becomes a persistent menace to the local population. In India, in some districts, between two and three hundred natives have been slain in a single year, close to a thousand in the whole country. Many villages have been deserted entirely because of the large numbers of deaths caused by these fearful man-eaters.

TIGER LEGENDS

There are many remarkable legends told about tigers in India. According to some tales, the tiger is in reality a human being who has been transformed into an animal. Many natives also believe that the tiger holds the ghosts of its victims in thrall. The spirits of those men that have been killed and eaten by a tiger, the natives say, sit on the great cat's head and go everywhere with it. Not only do they warn the tiger against danger but, entertaining malice toward their fellow men, they aid the beast in destroying them.

APPEASING THE TIGER'S SPIRIT IN SIBERIA

In Siberia, too, the tiger is greatly feared, the natives considering it to be favoured by their gods. When the author went to Amurland, in eastern Siberia, to hunt for tigers, he engaged a native of the Golde tribe, a Mongoloid clan, as a guide, but was told there were certain formalities that had to be complied with before the guide would leave his village.

The night before the hunting party left, a tiger feast was held in the village's largest hut and a shaman or witch doctor had to be hired to officiate. He came decked in all manner of trinkets and feathers to conduct the ceremony. A priestly fee, payable in liquor, was asked in advance, but kerosene proved acceptable as a substitute. A place was cleared on the floor, and the shaman went into as wild a dance as you could imagine. The air was thick with the smoke of evil-smelling tobacco and the babble of a strange tongue was everywhere as the party began in true Oriental fashion.

Suddenly the shaman stopped in his mad dance and began to sway unsteadily; the great spirit of the forest was entering his body. Everyone fell silent. The flickering wicks of the few smoky home-made lamps burned dimly on as the shaman sank slowly to the floor and was still. Presently he got to his knees and started to hop around like a rabbit, the sweat pouring down his face. He stopped in front of the author and seized his arm. Now the shaman coughed violently until a small white stone fell from his mouth into the author's hand. That was a guarantee that we would get one great white rabbit.

After an interval of about an hour, the shaman went into an even more fantastic dance. Again he was seized by a trance, but this time he crawled around like a bear and coughed up a large brown stone. It was now assured that the author would get a big brown bear.

The finale came at midnight. Previously, the dances had been wild and fantastic, but this one was weird and violent—the spirit of the tiger had entered. The shaman time and again literally hit the ceiling, crashed down on the floor, then bounced up again like a ball. After the trance he sprang through the air in great leaps. He visited the author three times, on each occasion coughing up a stone in the author's hand.

Now there was great rejoicing. Three tigers had been added to our bag. Forgiveness was asked of the tigers with the explanation that the natives needed the money and the foreigners would get the animals anyhow even if one of the Golde people did not act as guide.

It seems only fair to add that the author did get one big white rabbit, a giant brown bear that for some unexplainable reason had left its den in midwinter, and three beautiful Siberian tigers, two of which can be seen on exhibition at the American Museum of Natural History.

HUNTING THE TIGER

For any big-game hunter, the tiger is a great prize. There are a fair number of ways to kill it. The natives of India often favour a pitfall, but Westerners prefer high-powered rifles.

Sometimes tigers are shot from a platform erected in a tree close to a tethered animal. The most popular method of hunting tigers, however, is from the backs of elephants. A well-trained shikaree (sportsman's) elephant will stand the charge of a tiger while the hunters shoot it down. Occasionally the elephant will even rush to meet the tiger, much to the discomfort of the hunters in the howdah. The tiger will often roar when hit, though some say that the female remains silent.

TIGERS BIG AND SMALL

Although tigers are not found over nearly so wide a range as lions, they show much more variation from place to place. The typical Indian or Bengal tiger weighs about four hundred pounds. It may measure nine feet or longer (one-third of this is the tail). Long, narrow black stripes mark its limbs and body, which are tawny yellow in colour, fading to whitish on the under parts. The Caucasian tiger has brownish stripes, while the fur of the Siberian cat is lighter in colour and, in keeping with the climate, the hair is longer, thicker, and more luxuriant. Occasionally, a completely black or white tiger is born in an average litter.

The tigers of India and the more northern parts of the range are the largest and strongest of all. The Siberian tiger, giant of the species, reaches a total length of over thirteen feet and, if it is fat, will weigh over 650 pounds; the average male stands three feet at the shoulder, and weighs some 500 pounds. The smallest is the Bali tiger. In captivity, tigers have lived as long as twenty-five years.

JAGUARS—BIGGEST CATS OF THE NEW WORLD

The Jaguar, *Panthera (Jaguarius) onca*, is the New World's biggest cat. A sturdy, powerful creature, it may be six or eight feet long, overall, and weigh up to 250 pounds. No wonder the people of Mexico and Central America call the jaguar *el tigre*, and make a hasty retreat when they glimpse its tawny, black-spotted form in some dense jungle thicket. Among the cats, only the lion and tiger are larger than the jaguar.

Although this great, dangerous beast has disappeared from many of the places it once haunted, it is still found from Patagonia all the way through South and Central America, and as far north as Texas, New Mexico, and Arizona in the United States. Commonest in the tropical lowlands, where it often dwells in the marshes, it will make its home in arid and mountainous regions as well.

At night, the jaguar's deep, throaty roar wakes the jungle and fills its inhabitants with terror. No living creature is secure from the big cat's savage assault. Along the rivers it will tackle the alligator or the huge capybara, giant of the rodent race. It will pounce upon the turtle, turn it over, and rip it out of its shell. A strong swimmer, the jaguar often will not abandon the intended victim that seeks safety in the water. Even the monkeys in the trees sense imminent danger when they hear the lithe cat snarl, for they know it can climb and leap from branch to branch with impressive agility. The peccaries, wild pigs of the jungle, are a special favourite of the jaguar's, and domestic stock, too, frequently falls prey to it.

Every now and then the jaguar decides it would like a fish dinner. So it looks for a low branch that reaches out over a stream, or a rock that offers equally convenient access to the water. Fishermen might well envy the jaguar its easy angling technique. Resting on the comfortable perch it has selected, the cat extends its paw into the water and scoops up the fish. There are reports that the jaguar uses its tail as a lure, but there is some doubt about this.

There is, however, sufficient evidence to prove that the jaguar does on occasion attack man. It is the only American animal that becomes a man-eater by habit. Not every jaguar will kill people—only certain individuals are guilty. Instances of such attacks are becoming less common; the cats seem to be learning to avoid the man with the gun.

A DANGEROUS SPORT

Hunting the jaguar is a dangerous sport, but many consider it worth the risk because the animal's pelt is valuable. Dogs are used to track the big cat and bring it to bay.

Although the animal is a fast runner, it soon gets winded. Like the cougar, it will sometimes go up a tree, where it can be shot. But some jaguars prefer to stay on the ground and fight. Even when wounded they will tear apart any dog that comes too close. The hunter himself must be wary of a sudden, desperate charge by the enraged beast.

"TIGER" OF THE NEW WORLD

The jaguar is a fierce, predatory cat of North and South America. At first glance, it looks like a leopard, but one can see that its head is larger, its body heavier and broader, and the rosettes on its coat are wider. The jaguar is a good swimmer, and likes the water. With enviable ease, it sits by a stream, dips its great paw into the water, and brings up a fish dinner. Peccaries, sloths, and capybaras are among its favourite victims.

THE CHILDREN AND THE JAGUAR

We are indebted to Humboldt, a great German naturalist of the last century, for many realistic views of the intimate lives of South America's animals. Perhaps the most famous of his accounts is the picturesque story of an unferocious big cat—the "Ferdinand" of the jaguars.

Humboldt tells us of two Indian children who were playing in a small clearing in the deep forest. Suddenly, out of the dark shadows of the jungle, came a jaguar. The beast started to leap and gambol around the children, as though it wanted to join in their play. The children were fascinated as they watched the big, sleek, yellow-and-black animal gleaming in the bright sunlight. Closer and closer it bounded to the trusting children.

Accidentally perhaps, or possibly in play, the jaguar bumped into the younger of the two and gave the child a gentle pat. But the claws were unsheathed and they scratched the child's forehead. Blood began to flow. The other child immediately seized a stick and smacked the aguar in the face. The much-surprised animal slunk off into the forest and was never heard of again.

Fact or fiction? Probably the latter, for the jaguar is a ferocious beast and the story has a pattern typical of folklore. Still, strange things happen in the animal world; nor should we forget that Humboldt himself had reason to accept the tale as true.

A HANDSOME CAT

One of the handsomest of all cats, the jaguar has a coat that is rich yellow or tawny in colour, marked with a chain of black spots down the back, bordered by five rows of black rosettes, running lengthwise on the sides. Its tail, limbs, and head are heavily spotted and lined with black. The larger head, stocky and more robust form, shorter tail, and larger rosettes serve to distinguish it from the leopard. At least a dozen subspecies are known. Black jaguars are not unusual, especially in the valley of the Amazon. There are spots present even on these, but only a good light will reveal them.

The jaguar may mate at any time of the year. About one hundred days later, two to four kittens are born. They are more heavily spotted than the adults, but lack rosettes. The male appears to be a permanent member of the family; a good husband and a providing father, he is ready to feed and protect his young at all times. But when the kittens are a year old, they are capable of shifting for themselves, and when they reach three years they are old enough to breed. Their life span is twenty years.

CHEETAHS—FASTEST ANIMALS ON LAND

The Cheetah, Guepard, or Hunting Leopard, *Acinonyx jubatus*, of Asia and Africa, is the fastest land animal on earth. Leaping from a position of rest, it can reach a speed of forty-five miles per hour in two seconds. But that is not even the top rate of this lightning-swift cat; timed by a stop watch, it has actually raced along at seventy miles per hour!

Although the cheetah is able to outrun a greyhound, it cannot keep up its extraordinary pace for long. Four or five hundred yards would be its limit, and then it is pretty well winded. But still it is evident that so speedy and big a cat—it is as large as the leopard—can, if trained, be a remarkable help to hunters.

Long, long ago the rajahs of India recognized the cheetah's remarkable abilities and put them to use. They found that the cat, if taken too young, was not aggressive enough. What was needed was a cheetah that had learned the savage ways of its kind, yet could be trained to respond to its master's cues.

The Indian hunters learned there were certain trees to which the wild cheetahs came to whet their claws. Here the men would lie in wait for the unsuspecting animals. They ensnared the beasts by means of nooses, carried them off despite their savage resistance, and put them through a rigid course of training. The result? Cats that hunted like dogs.

HUNTING WITH A CHEETAH

A hunt with a cheetah was one of the most thrilling spectacles that yesterday's India had to offer. The hunters carried the tame cheetah afield in a cart; they had the animal hooded like a falcon. When they discovered the game—usually gazelles or black bucks, the common long-horned antelopes of India—they would whip off the cat's hood and direct its sharp eyes to the intended victim. Taking advantage of every available scrap of cover, the cheetah would creep to within a quarter of a mile of the unsuspecting quarry and then hurl itself towards it at top speed.

Gazelles and antelopes are no mean runners. When they know their lives are in the balance, they will put every ounce of energy, every dodge and device they possess, into a great, heart-breaking effort to save themselves.

In endurance these creatures are certainly superior to the cheetah. If they can stay ahead of it long enough, they will live to run again another day. But in the early part of the contest the cheetah has the advantage of greater speed.

In the crucial first few hundred yards of these life-and-death races, the buck would plunge forward with each muscle straining and an agonized look in its large eyes, the huge spotted cat following relentlessly at its heels. If the cheetah had a good start, the end was not long in coming. The feline's bared fangs, once they reached the antelope's throat, could tear it to shreds in a matter of seconds.

LIKE A FLASH OF LIGHTNING

Swiftest runner of all land animals, the cheetah, or hunting leopard, can run seventy miles per hour in an initial burst of speed. After four or five hundred yards, however, it slows down. In India, where the cheetah is trained for the hunt like a dog, it must catch its prey in this first speed; otherwise, the sought-after antelope and gazelle, with their greater endurance, will stay in the lead. The cheetah, though a true cat, has the long, slender legs and unsheathed claws found in dogs.

MOST DOGLIKE OF THE CATS

The most like a dog of all the cats, the cheetah is superbly equipped for running. It has long, slender legs, so that it stands two and one-half feet high at the shoulder. Its feet are narrow but large. The claws in particular remind us of the dog's—thev are stout and always unsheathed, for the cheetah, unlike other cats, cannot draw them back completely.

Its body, admirably muscled but lithe, is streamlined, so that it offers little resistance to the air as the animal makes its headlong dashes. The long tail aids it in turning.

The cheetah is becoming a rarity in Asia, although it was once found in many places, from the Caspian Sea to Sumatra. In Africa, too, it is disappearing, along with the big game, as man encroaches on its ancient domain, but you may still glimpse it in East Africa, Senegal, the Sudan, Transvaal, Bechuanaland, and Rhodesia.

This feline spends its resting hours in tall grass or lairs among the rocks. Departing from the habits of many of its kind, it is abroad during daylight hours, even in the hot season. It hunts by sight rather than smell, and bright moonlit nights will bring it out of its hideout. Usually two or three animals travel in company; occasionally parties of four or five have been seen together, but we believe these are family groups. Medium-sized and small antelopes like the duiker and the impala are the game the cheetah favours.

Compared to its deep-voiced cousin the tiger, the cheetah can hardly be called a noisy animal. In a pleased and restful mood, it will purr, reminding us of a house cat. Tame, the animal is esteemed by its keepers for its friendliness.

SOUGHT FOR ITS PELT

A handsome animal, the cheetah yields a valuable pelt to those who hunt it down. Its close fur is sandy brown in colour and covered with a good many solid black spots. In the King Cheetah of Rhodesia, an exceptionally large, fine species, the spots tend to fuse together into stripes. (The true leopard has rosettes instead.) There is a black streak on each side of the beast's face. On the nape of its neck it has a short mane. An adult weighs about one hundred pounds and has a total length of about seven feet, of which two and one-half are the tail.

When pursued by dogs, the wild cheetah will take to a tree. One surprised its hunters by going two-thirds of the way up a tall, straight coconut palm before it was slain.

Cheetahs have lived in zoos for nearly sixteen years, but they could hardly survive that long in the wild.

Sea Lions, Walruses, and Seals—
Mammals with Finfeet

WHENEVER we watch seals, we cannot help marvelling at the difference between the way they move in the water and the way they travel on land. In the water, they are all amazing speed and grace, scarcely raising a ripple on the surface as they streak forward. On land, they are clumsy, awkward waddlers.

This contrast is typical of all the creatures in the order Pinnipedia —the sea lions, walruses, and true seals. We call them pinnipeds, or— if you prefer a more recognizable term—finfeet. They are land-and-water animals with finned flippers; warm-blodded mammals specially adapted for life in the water. Unlike the whales and porpoises, the pinnipeds are not entirely independent of land; they spend part of their existence on the seashore or on floating ice. As for speedy travel in the water, these finfeet are hardly the equals of the whales. On the other hand, seals and walruses have greater agility in the water— they can manoeuvre with perfect safety in the pounding surf around ragged rocks.

A SEA-CHANGE

Distant ages ago the ancestors of these animals were exclusively creatures of the land. No doubt they hunted along the shores and beaches for food left by the receding tides.

How long do you think it took the ancestral finfeet to change from land-bound animals to seafaring mariners? A great span of time indeed, it must have been—probably more than several million years. (It takes about a million years to develop a species.) Gradually, little by little, the ancient pinnipeds went farther and farther into the water. By degrees they became streamlined and fashioned for a life in the deep.

Dire necessity may have driven them to this change, as whole continents were gradually swallowed up by the sea, and animal life either took to the water or perished.

Today, the finfeet as a group are at their most abundant in northern waters; however, we find them in all seas except the warmer parts of the Indian Ocean. As we have seen, these creatures have streamlined bodies to cut down water resistance as much as possible, and their fore and hind limbs have been modified into flippers. The animals are usually covered with hair or fur to keep them warm in their Arctic home, but we notice this difference among them—the walruses and true seals are more thoroughly insulated with a heavy layer of blubber than the sea lions. Consequently, the walruses and true seals are less dependent on a warm coat of hair.

Eared Seals or Sea Lions

Perhaps you have been wondering about such terms as "true seals", "eared seals", "sea lions", and the like. How are they similar, how do they differ? The true seals are the ones most highly specialized for life in the water. As part of this more advanced adaptation, they do not have outside ears.

But there are other creatures that look very much like these true seals, with one noticeable difference—they have external ears, and are called eared seals. Another name for eared seals is "sea lions" (they are not lions in any sense at all; they are lions of the sea). The hallmark, then, of the eared seals or sea lions is that they are less highly adapted for life in the sea. Not only do they have a small external ear; they are superior to the true seals when it comes to moving about on land. The eared seals are able to rotate their hind limbs forward to support the body as they progress on land; their front flippers are large, long, and for the most part naked.

The sea lions have short, sleek hair and tight-fitting fur which varies in colour from species to species—generally some shade of grey or brown. These animals—they make up the family Otariidae—are particularly given to living in herds; they are even more sociable than other kinds of seals. The adults are of course thoroughly at home in the water, but the young, born on land, must learn how to swim. It is rather strange that though there are sea lions in the North and South

Pacific, the South Atlantic and other southern waters, they have never reached the North Atlantic.

EATING TOOLS AND HABITS

Before we turn to some of the different kinds of sea lions, it will be interesting to get some notion of what seals in general eat and how they eat. They are all great fish-eaters—fish is their staple food. But, depending on the species, they add crustaceans, squids, and even shellfish to their daily rations. Each side of both jaws is lined with interlocking rows of sharp-pointed teeth—ideal weapons for seizing and holding their finny prey.

The seal has no broad-crowned molars for crushing and grinding food. Consequently the animal must swallow food whole—generally the prey is eaten while it is still alive, for that matter. Many seals also bolt quantities of stones and gravel, not, as some sailors more or less jocularly suggest, for ballast, but to help mill their food. This habit reminds us of certain grain-eating birds, which need gravel to grind the hard corn in the gizzard. Of course, the quantity of stone or gravel that most birds will take is trifling compared to what the seals require. On the average, sixteen pounds of stones—some as large as a hen's egg— are taken from a sea lion's stomach.

Examination of the stomach contents of the seals that travel in great herds yields another interesting bit of information: herring is the mainstay of their diet. The Leopard Seal of the Antarctic is the only species that feeds on warm-blooded animal life. It has large, vicious-looking teeth for cutting and tearing flesh; but even this seal lacks crushing molars, and it must bolt penguins and other sea birds more or less in big chunks. Still, it cannot digest the feathers and must get rid of them through the mouth after the meat has been dissolved.

NORTHERN FUR SEALS

The Northern Fur Seal, or Sea Bear, *Callorhinus alascanus*, also known as the Alaska Fur Seal, has the finest fur of all the seal tribe. (The term "sea bear" is merely a popular name. The northern fur seal is an eared seal—not a bear at all.) Of medium size, the northern fur seal is about six feet long, with a weight of five hundred to seven hundred pounds. These figures apply to grown bulls; females are much smaller.

The northern fur seal is famous for the thick, soft fur that underlies the longer, glistening guard hairs. Fur processers remove the coarse outer hairs, leaving the silky plush of the inner coat—the commercially valuable sealskin. The bull is black, with a cape of grey hair on the shoulders and a swollen neck. The female is mainly grey.

MATING HABITS OF THE NORTHERN FUR SEAL

Every spring since time immemorial the northern fur seals have left their Pacific haunts to converge on the small, bleak Pribilof Islands in the North Pacific to breed. Nothing keeps them from following this inexorable routine; though the animals were slaughtered in thousands for their fur, those that escaped always returned to the islands to mate.

Once the breeding season is over and the pups are raised, the fur

PROVIDER OF THE CHOICEST SEALSKIN

The softest and most beautiful sealskins that we use commercially come from the northern fur seal or sea bear. This elegant fur is really the inner layer of the animal's fur; above it is an outer layer of coarse hair which must first be removed. The islands where vast hordes of the northern fur seals congregate each spring to breed were once scenes of mass slaughter by get-rich-quick sealers. Without the legal protection now enforced, this splendid fur-bearing animal might have been completely exterminated.

The tiger is the typical big cat of Asia. Matching the lion in size and surpassing it in strength and cunning, the tiger is a bloodthirsty, wanton killer.   *See page 587*

[5-13]

The jaguar is the New World's biggest cat, and no living creature is secure from its savage assault. Ranging from the south-western United States through Central and South America, it is most common in the tropical lowlands.   *See page 592*

[5-13A]

A large bull walrus may be 10 or 11 feet long and weigh between 2,000 and 3,000 pounds. Both sexes have tusks but the male's are heavier, extra-large ones measuring up to 38 inches and weighing 11 pounds. The thick, rough almost hairless hide is prized by the Eskimos for making shelters and covering their boats.   *See page 608*

seal puts out to sea again and does not go ashore until the following spring. The fur seal winters in southern waters at latitudes roughly parallel with California.

The northern fur seal is a herd animal. The bulls have large harems, usually numbering forty or fifty cows—though this figure may be as large as a hundred cows. In April or May the bulls push ahead of the main herd, clamber on land, and take up their positions on the island shores. The first-comers get the best places—but they must fight to hold them. Each station covers an area of seventy-five to a hundred square feet. The choice locations are naturally those near the water's edge.

From the middle of June to mid-July, the mature females, now heavy with young, begin to arrive; they are met by the nearest bull and escorted to his station. The cows give birth to a single pup within a few hours of their arrival—or within a day or two at most. The biggest and strongest bulls get the most females; the weaker move into "idle-bull" position behind the main harems and take what opportunity offers them. The "bachelors", too young to mate, congregate in small, solitary groups.

Once a bull has established his position, he never leaves his harem until it is time to depart from the island. He trusts neither his "wives" nor his neighbours; so, from two to three months he goes without food, continually uttering threatening bellows as warnings to any bull that might challenge his proprietary rights or dally with any notions of conjugal poaching.

By August all the pups are born, and the females have mated again. The old bulls, gaunt from their prolonged and self-imposed fasting, brawling, and guarding, abandon their truculence and assume their more normal group mode of life for another year. However, the mating season is not quite over for all the members of the colony. About this time thousands of virgin females, which begin to breed at two years of age, come ashore to mate and are excitedly met by idle-bulls that have more or less patiently bided their time.

The pups, born with wide-open blue eyes, learn to swim by the time they are six to eight weeks old. They are weaned in three or four months, about the time when the main body of the colony puts out to sea. On their winter cruise, seals travel some six thousand miles and are subject to attack by the killer whale, which may swallow as many as twenty or more seals in quick succession. The mortality rate among seals is particularly high during their first three years; nearly fifty per cent of the pups never reach maturity. There are many deaths from accidents on the breeding grounds, and, apart from the losses inflicted by sharks and killer whales, some animals perish during severe storms.

The life span of fur seals is about twenty years, but few of them ever die of old age. Still, twenty-one-year-old females have occasionally been seen with pups, and some bulls have lived to be twenty-two years old.

THE FUR TRADE AND ITS EXCESSES

The same urge that forces the fur seals to forge on to the Pribilof Islands to perpetuate their kind has often led them to their deaths at the hands of sealers. For the animals the story has been one of turmoil, tragedy, and death; for man, it has meant great sums of money. Twice the fur seals have come near extermination, but today three million of them visit the islands of the North Pacific every spring to breed. The size and activity of these vast gatherings of wild life are almost incredible.

The Russians took over the Pribilof Islands in 1786, and soon Russian fortune-seekers swarmed over the islands, slaughtering the seals without stint and persecuting and even murdering the natives as well. Thousands of seals were clubbed to death and left to rot on the beaches until the air was foul and contaminated with the stench of their bodies. At last the Russian government learned what was going on and put a stop to the ruthless waste of the world's most valuable source of fur. Thus the seals were given a breathing spell.

However, when the United States purchased the islands from Russia in 1867 the sealing rights were leased to unscrupulous sealers who readily copied the sordid pattern of the early Russian sealers. With more modern equipment and faster ships available, the massacre of the seals was even greater than under the Russians. Sealers from other nations carried the slaughter to the high seas, until the point was reached where four out of every five seals were being exterminated. On one occasion a thousand baby seals, whose mothers had been slain, were counted dead on the shore.

Conservationists brought pressure to bear on Washington, and in 1887 England, Russia, Japan, France, Germany, Sweden, and Norway got together with the United States to frame a convention to stop unrestricted sealing in the North Pacific, but the treaty was not ratified. The relentless slaughter continued until the herds were reduced to less than 124,000.

Then, suddenly and without friction, the North Pacific Sealing Convention was signed by the four most interested powers. Their nationals were forbidden to seal in the Pacific north of latitude 30° north. To increase the number of the animals, they were given five years of grace from sealing. At the end of this period, they were to be harvested by the United States and a division made of the proceeds of the skins sold at auction.

Auction sales now total about $2,500,000, and dressed, dyed skins sold at the auction fetch an average of about eighty-five dollars apiece. Nowadays twenty-five thousand to thirty thousand can safely be harvested each year. Oil and other products are rendered from the carcasses. Bachelor seals are mostly used for pelts; since these are the young males who have not reached the age when they have mating brawls, their fur is likely to be in top condition. Old males are never used, and females are kept for breeding.

The Southern Fur Seal, *Arctocephalus* ("bear-headed"), varies in size from about five and one-half feet in length and 450 pounds in weight for the Townsend Fur Seal, one of the rarest forms, to approximately seven feet in length and eight hundred pounds in weight for the South African Cape Seal.

Once widely and liberally distributed along the Pacific shores of Mexico and the coastal waters of South America, Africa, and Australia, the southern fur seal is similar in appearance to its northern cousin. The southern variety differs in skeletal structure and in its fur, which is of somewhat inferior grade. There are seven geographical species, all of them reduced to the border of extinction.

CALIFORNIA SEA LIONS—EASILY TRAINED

The California Sea Lion, *Zalophus californianus*, is the trained seal of the stage and the one frequently seen in zoological gardens and circuses. A moderately large, dark-brown seal with thick, close hair and a poor grade of short underfur, it is found along the Pacific coast of North America from southern Mexico to northern California. Males measure eight feet long and weigh up to six hundred pounds.

The life history of California sea lions is much like that of the northern fur seal. Less jealous of their harems, the bulls even take time off for feeding. Though fond of fish, the sea lion is even more partial to squids and is thus no serious menace to food fishes.

TRAINED SEALS AND THEIR ANTICS

Most of us have seen performing seals and been amazed at their ability to learn tricks. As it happens, they are not true seals but eared seals or sea lions—the California species. Their genuine aptitude for training comes from their love of sport and play, a well-developed sense of balance, and their desire for attention. They are extremely active, and anything in the nature of exercise or exhibitionism appeals to them —especially if there is a fish as a reward in sight. They have a fair share of intelligence and can size up a situation with very little instruction.

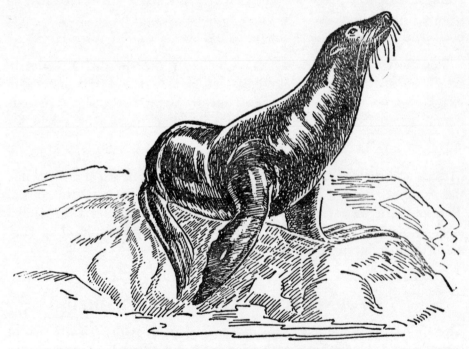

THE SEA LION—EVER-POPULAR ENTERTAINER

The California sea lion, found all along the Pacific coast of North America, is the playful performer of theatres and circuses. Easily trained, intelligent, and equipped with a good sense of balance, this animal will, for the sake of fish and applause, run through a delightful array of tricks. The California sea lion has small external ears, and hind limbs which can be rotated forward, a boon to the creature when it moves about on land.

Given the sea lion's sense of co-ordination, the long flexible neck is just right for balancing a big rubber ball on the tip of the animal's nose. The sea lion can even be taught to play a tune on a row of trumpets, but this is a matter of routine practice; the creature has no notion that it is producing a tune.

There is no doubt that most mammals are affected by swing music. Sea lions respond readily, and with a little practice soon learn to sway and even dance to a tune. But it is the reward at the end of the act that the seal really has in mind. Its motto is: "No reward, no show."

STELLER'S SEA LION—IT MAY WEIGH A TON

Steller's or the Northern Sea Lion, *Eumetopias jubata*, an enormous brownish creature, is the largest of all sea lions. Steller, the German scientist who first discovered this animal, named it *Leo marinus* ("lion of the sea"), as he noted the greatly swollen neck of the males and the leonine eyes with their golden pupil and white iris. Full-grown males may reach a length of thirteen feet and weigh as much as fifteen hundred to two thousand pounds. The female is less than half the size of the bull.

This great sea lion has much the same habits as the fur seal, though the colonies and harems are not so large. The bull is not jealous and does not fight so desperately over his harem as a fur seal bull; in fact, there is more fidelity among the females. When a battle does ensue, the fighters pay no attention to the pups underfoot and many are mercilessly crushed to death.

OPEN-EYED BABIES

The baby sea lion comes into the world with its big blue eyes open —at least they are wide open almost immediately after birth. It soon gains control of its limbs and romps among the yellow hulks of the adults. In a few days it can move swiftly—as indeed it must if it is to escape being crushed by the battling bulls. Weighing between thirty-five and fifty pounds at birth, the pups will weigh about one hundred pounds two months later. The front part of the animal develops more rapidly than the rest of the body; an adult male sea lion has a large, swollen neck and enormous shoulders.

TEACHING A BABY TO SWIM

Familiar as we are with the sea lions' gracefulness in the water, it seems incredible that they have to be taught to swim. The baby sea lion does have to learn to swim; we are told that the mother picks up the pup by the back of the neck and carries it to the water for its introductory swimming lesson. At first the baby struggles in the surf—but by the time it is two months old, it ploughs proudly through the breakers and rides the waves like a veteran.

With the end of summer and the close of the breeding season, the big brown animal leaves the cold, damp, icy coast of Alaska and travels south to the warmer waters of Mexico. Its summer range is the rocky coast of Alaska north to the Bering Strait.

This large sea lion was hunted extensively for its blubber; the hide and intestines were used for a number of purposes, including the manufacture of raincoats. The present laws prohibit indiscriminate killing of sea lions, but fishermen may destroy them when they interfere with fishing activities. A census of sea lions on the California coast in 1947 showed a population of 5,666 Steller's sea lions and 3,050 California sea lions.

OTHER EARED SEALS OR SEA LIONS

The Japanese Sea Lion is now believed to be extinct, and has been relegated to museum status. The South American Sea Lion, also known as *lobo del mar* (Spanish for "wolf of the sea"), is found on both sides of the South American continent; it has maintained itself better than other seals in South American waters. The male Australian Sea Lion differs from other sea lions in having a patch of yellow on the crown of the head and back of the neck. The little-known Hooker's Sea Lion, of the Auckland Islands south of New Zealand, has a flattened head and a comparatively long muzzle.

Walruses—at Home on Arctic Ice Packs

The walrus lives in the loneliest and most desolate region in the world. Its days, spent on floating ice, are beset with bitter cold, raging snowstorms, and fierce blizzards. Strangely enough—from our point of view—the walrus seems to enjoy this kind of existence. Few other creatures could maintain themselves amidst such drastic conditions.

Not many mammals are so grotesquely ungainly as the walrus, with its crude, wrinkled exterior, yet it has a majestic grandeur all the same. It was born on a cake of ice, covered with a blanket of late-spring snow, and rocked to sleep by stormy winds, with the sound of the grinding ice-packs in its ears. Though fat and pudgy, its little pug face has an appealing beauty to the two-thousand-pound mother walrus; awkwardly but lovingly she tucks her baby's little body between her flippers with her long, gleaming tusks.

CLUMSY LORD OF THE ICE-FLOES

The droll-looking walrus serenely spends its life amid raging blizzards and the most intensely cold climates found anywhere on earth. Generally peaceful, this creature uses its fierce tusks for fighting the polar bear and the killer whale, and for obtaining its main food, shellfish. By scraping its tusks along the bottom of the sea, the walrus loosens the clams and other shellfish embedded in the sand. Pictured above is the Pacific walrus.

The bitter-cold winter storms are of little consequence to the walrus mother—they are all part of her life. Her eyesight is not of the best, but she has a sharp sense of smell and is ever on the alert for the prowling polar bear.

As one of these marauders approaches, she rises to her full height, and her neck bulges as she utters a deep, guttural, challenging bellow of defiance. She swings around to follow the circling bear; one step too close, and with a flash down comes the full force of her tusks. Not so easily dismayed, the bear continues his attack. Occasionally, by dint of persistent harassing, the bear will manage to rob the mother of her child; but the chances are that he will crawl away to lick his wounds, a sadder and perhaps wiser animal.

But it is really the killer whale that is the deadly foe of the walrus. Caught in the sea away from the friendly shelter of the ice, a mother walrus will wage a desperate struggle with a school of these tigers of the sea to protect her young. But as fast as she sinks her harpoon-like tusks into a whale, another swings into action and it becomes doubtful whether she can save her own life.

The ice itself can become a hazard. The ice packs may jam into a vast, grinding mass fifty miles wide where not even a walrus could survive; however, few of the animals are ever trapped this way. Most creatures that travel in herds have their sentinels posted, but when a herd of walruses are enjoying a blissful sleep and snoring contentedly, no one is left to watch for approaching danger. However, from time to time a member of the group will wake up with a start and look around before continuing its deep slumber. At the first unusual sound the whole herd springs into action.

The combined roar and bellowing produced by a herd of disturbed walruses can be heard for several miles. On occasion their hoarse roar has warned ships in time to escape being shattered on fog-misted icebergs.

LIFE OF A WALRUS

The Walrus, *Odobenus*, or "whale horse", as it was known to the Norsemen, is easily recognized by its long ivory tusks. They may reach a length of thirty inches—in fact, the extra-large ones measure up to thirty-eight inches and weigh a good eleven pounds. Both male and female have tusks, but they are heavier in the bulls. An enormous creature, the walrus has a practically hairless skin which is wrinkled and roughened like the bark of an old oak tree. Large males are ten to eleven feet long and weigh between two thousand and three thousand pounds.

The walruses, which make up the family Odobenidae, are like the sea lions in some ways, different in other ways. Walruses have the same kind of flippers, for example—they can rotate the rear flippers in order to get about more easily on land. However, the walruses, unlike the sea lions, have no outside ears.

Though this animal is a slow, clumsy swimmer, it is big enough to protect itself from most natural enemies with the exception of the killer whale. Feeding on the sea bottom, it uses its tusks to dig up clams and other shellfish. It cracks the shells with its back teeth but then swallows the shells along with the meat. Crushed by action of the stomach and small stones, the meat is then digested and the empty shells are ejected through the mouth.

The walruses enjoy a family life that is more peaceful than that of the sea lions. Bulls, calves, and cows mingle together, albeit in a somewhat quarrelsome manner. Discord arises chiefly from their dislike of being disturbed when sleeping. One walrus may accidentally nudge another, whereupon the offended sleeper wakes up with a mighty, trumpet-like roar and takes a prodigious slap at its nearest neighbour. The latter, in turn, utters an ear-splitting bellow and passes the blow on to the accompaniment of similar deafening sounds of protest—until the whole colony is in a turmoil.

The cow walrus has but one calf at a time, giving birth on the ice-floes in May or June, nearly a year after mating. As we have seen, she has a strongly developed maternal instinct and will sell her life dearly in the protection of her calf. Once aroused, a walrus will charge any suspicious stranger that comes near. Male and female separate in July but they are found together again in late August or September.

During its early life, the baby walrus rides on its mother's back in the water and holds fast with its flippers when she submerges for food. The young walrus is dependent on its mother for nourishment until it is two years old, when its tusks are long enough for digging clams. Until this time it must live on the mother's milk.

The walrus is generally restricted to the ice-floes and rocky coast of the Arctic Ocean, although it has been recorded as far south as Newfoundland and northern Scotland. There are two named forms of walrus: the Atlantic Walrus and the Pacific Walrus. At one time walruses were hunted extensively for their blubber; but nowadays there are so few left that such ventures are no longer worth while commercially. The Eskimos use the hide, which is from half an inch to three inches thick, to make their shelters and cover their boats. The meat and fat serve for food, and the ivory tusks are made into tools and carved ornaments.

Earless Seals, or True Seals

The true seals are strongly adapted for a water-dwelling existence. To begin with, they lack an external ear. The hind limbs are modified into flippers for swimming, but they extend straight out behind; the seal cannot rotate them forward for greater support on land. As for the forelimbs, they have developed into short paddles used mainly for balancing and turning in the water. The entire animal, including the limbs, flippers, and the short tail, is covered with short, coarse hair, without any trace of underfur. The true seals (they make up the family Phocidae) are sometimes called "hair seals".

Seals must leave the water to breed, and to bear their young, which remain on land for several weeks before being taught to swim. The true seals have spread to all the oceans of the world; yet, despite the fact that they are primarily ocean-dwellers, they have ascended many large rivers and even entered inland lakes. Swimming on the surface and breathing normally, the animals have an average heartbeat rate of one hundred per minute; when they dive the heart action slows up to ten beats per minute.

Seal meat and blubber are the Eskimo's chief sources of food during the cold winter months, and he uses the seal skin to make clothing. It is in the northern regions that seals are found in the greatest abundance. Commercial sealers now plunder the great herds of seals in the North Atlantic and annually slaughter many thousands for leather and oil.

HARBOUR SEALS—SWIFT AND SHY

The Harbour Seal, *Phoca vitulina*, is the common seal of the temperate and colder regions of the Northern Hemisphere. This small species is frequently seen along reefs, around coastal islands, and in sheltered harbours. Never straying far from land, it ascends large rivers, often beyond the influence of the tide, and occasionally makes its appearance in inland lakes. A harbour seal is capable of travelling twelve or fifteen miles per hour—but it cannot keep up this speed for more than half a mile.

The colour pattern varies quite a bit. The normal shade is yellowish grey spotted with dark brown, but the fur may intergrade to black spotted with white. The full-grown male easily measures five feet long and weighs one hundred pounds or more. The first coat of the harbour seal is white and woolly, but this is shed immediately after— or even before—birth in the spring. The newborn pup, which is nursed for four or five weeks, has a cry that reminds us of a lamb bleating.

While the harbour seal does not congregate in large colonies, it is nevertheless fond of company. Family groups of two or three females with their young and a male or two are not uncommon. Apparently unable to sleep in the water, this seal comes ashore regularly to rest and sun itself on the rocks.

Having experienced man's assaults through many generations, the harbour seal is understandably shy and elusive. Yet it soon responds to kind treatment and protection, making a surprisingly affectionate pet for those living at the water's edge. However, not many of us would care to have a big, wet seal bringing mud into the house and taking possession of an upholstered couch or chair!

The harbour seal has a varied diet, feeding on tom cod (a small fish resembling the common cod), flounder, herring, pollack, and other fish as well as squids and octopus.

Experts now recognize six forms of harbour seal. The local subspecies dwell on the European and American sides of the Atlantic from Labrador to Maine and occasionally as far south as North Carolina, and in Asiatic and American coastal waters of the Pacific as far south as Baja California.

RINGED SEALS—MOST NORTHERLY OF MAMMALS

The Ringed Seal, *Phoca hispida*, ranges north probably farther than any other mammal; it is the common seal of the polar region, and we rarely find it south of the Arctic Ocean. Though similar in size and colour to the harbour seal, it is quite a different animal. The ringed seal's markings are a number of rings, or white spots with dark centres. In the Hudson Bay area it is most common along the east coast, where the Eskimos call it *netcheck*.

The ringed seal is able to submerge for about seven to nine minutes; in case of need, it can stay under water for twenty minutes without coming up for air. The seal needs about forty-five seconds to change the air in its lungs between normal submersions.

This seal is not a migrator; in northern waters, when the shore ice creeps out to sea, the animal keeps a breathing-hole open, visiting it periodically to rest and breathe. This habit sometimes means death for the seal—it is here that the Eskimo lies in wait to harpoon it when it makes its routine visit.

Before the spring thaw in March or April, either single or twin pups are born. The nursery is a burrow in the hard snow and has a tunnel connecting it with the breathing-hole in the ice. The newborn ringed seal is covered with soft, white, woolly fur, although even yearlings may still be whitish along the back.

HARP SEALS—GREAT HERDS OF THE NORTH ATLANTIC

The Harp Seal, Saddle-backed or Greenland Seal, *Phoca groenlandica*, is bigger than the harbour seal. Large bulls measure up to six feet in length and weigh between six hundred and eight hundred pounds. Despite persistent commercial hunting, the harp seal still occurs in large herds in the North Atlantic. It migrates with the seasons and in winter follows the floes of the open ice as far south as Newfoundland.

Thousands of young, each weighing about nine pounds, are born in March off the Grand Banks of Newfoundland; there is usually one in a litter, and twins are rare. Coarse, pale-grey hair replaces the white, woolly birthday coat in about four weeks, when the pups are ready to enter the water. Sealers call the baby seals "white-coats".

If we stop to think about it, we realize that this colour change has protective value. The newborn and those not yet able to swim are white, inconspicuous against the snow-covered ice packs on which they lie; the grey fur of the young that have taken to the water is far less noticeable than white would be in the sea. Incidentally, the harps or saddle stripes of the male (described later) are not completed until the fourth year.

During the early stages of infancy the young are left on the drifting ice while the parents go forth daily to fish. Since there may be several thousand offspring in a group, it is remarkable indeed that each mother should find her own pup at the close of day. Soon after the end of April the young "harps" have learned to swim and are catching fish for themselves. The herd now moves north and eventually reaches the coast of Greenland.

The harp seal feeds on whitefish, cod, and in part on crustaceans.

Descending to a depth of two hundred feet, it may stay under water twenty minutes at a time. This fast seal can cruise along at a maximum of twenty miles an hour, but its average speed is much less. In the autumn migrations the great herds at one time numbered as many as five hundred thousand head. More than one hundred thousand harp seals are still taken every year in the Arctic; the catch is valued at over $250,000,000. Oil and leather are the chief products.

THE HOODED SEAL BLOWS UP ITS "HOOD" WHEN EXCITED

Extending from the tip of the male hooded seal's nose to the top of its head is a bag or bladder of inflatable muscular tissue. Whenever the seal becomes excited, as during mating time, the bag swells up like a balloon. The hooded seal inhabits the waters of the North Atlantic and Arctic Oceans, where the harp seal is also found. But the hooded seal does not mingle with the harp, choosing to remain on floes well out in deep waters.

The male harp seal is light grey or yellowish white in colour, with characteristic bands of brown extending from the neck over the shoulders and down each side in the form of a saddle, or harp. The female differs from the male in size and colouring; she is smaller, and the dull-white or straw-coloured fur has indistinct back markings or lacks them completely.

GREY SEALS—WITH FACES ALMOST HUMAN

The Grey Seal, *Halichoerus grypus*, is the subject of many myths. In Scandinavian folklore there is a belief that the grey seal is the reincarnation of either a human soul or a fallen angel, and that some fearful retribution will fall upon the man who molests it.

Shetland Islanders tell of sea monsters called "Finns" that have the power to take on the shape of human beings. On winter nights they come ashore as grey seals to dance on the sands. They cast off their skins and act like men and women, but they cannot return to the sea without their skins. Some of the "Finn" women, so the legends tell us, were captured and married by the Shetlanders. There are islanders today who pride themselves on being descended from "Finn" women.

The Welsh have similar traditions, and so have the Irish—the Irish clan of Coneely is said to be directly descended from a seal-woman. In Scotland, too, there is a legendary folklore connected with the grey seal. The clan of MacOdrum, for example, was known as the "seal-eaters". The clan was supposed to have certain affinities with the grey seal. Some old-timers will beg for the front flippers of a grey seal which has been killed, though they are not interested in parts of any other species of seal. Apparently these flippers were the parts used in an ancient ceremonial feast—a pagan festival in honour of the Scandinavian god Odin.

BATTLES AT MATING TIME

Late in August or September the grey seal bulls crawl out on the rocky beaches where their ancestors have appeared for centuries. Here they sprawl in the sunshine. A week or so later the females drift ashore, and are greeted by the males. There is, as we might expect, considerable bellowing and competition between the males for possession of the females. Often fierce battles take place. Rolling from side to side, the bulls show their white teeth to competitors, and frequently inflict deep gashes in the necks of their adversaries.

Within a few hours after landing, the females give birth to a single calf clothed in long white fur. At birth a calf will weigh about thirty pounds. Two weeks later, its weight has increased to eighty-four pounds. The cows mate ten or twelve days after the calves are born.

Each bull has its own domain, which covers about one-tenth of an acre. While the males fight furiously for their territorial rights, they do not dominate the females. In fact, females are granted equal rights with the males and are not herded together by a jealous bull, as in the case of the sea lions. If a cow lands on a bull's domain and stays there, she is his—but if she chooses to cross over into another's field, he raises no objection and shows no further interest in her.

By November, peace reigns once more. The fighting and bellowing have ceased. The males live together in perfect harmony. A passing female does not attract even an uninterested glance.

BABY GREY SEALS

Grey seals, especially the pups, are almost human in appearance. Their big, round eyes seem to stare out of a comely round face with a most appealing expression. During its early days the pup gets full-time attention from the mother seal. She nurses it on milk, rich and yellow with butter-fat, for two or three weeks. During this time the devoted mother stays at home without food in order to guard and fondle her baby and even to scratch its back. With a little tummy full of rich milk, the pup may yawn, put the tip of a flipper in its mouth, murmuring contentedly like a child, and fall fast asleep.

It is curious that at first the calves can use their hind feet to propel themselves along, and flip them alternately like regular land mammals. Two or three days later they have lost this trait and never use the hind limbs again for progress on land. Many scientists hold that baby seals must be taught to swim. This is not exactly true. Young grey seals are born with a thick, woolly, white coat. They can swim from the very first, but the heavy swaddling clothes of the new-born infants are too absorbent to permit them to remain afloat long in the water.

The baby seals change their warm white clothes for the regular adult grey coats between the second and fourth week. They are weaned during the third week, when the cows are ready to go to sea, and they must feed themselves. For the next two weeks they live on their accumulated fat, but soon hunger drives them to sea, where they quickly learn to find food and swim in the shallow water.

Within a few days the young seals are out in the deep, fishing like veterans. They soon learn to catch molluscs and crustaceans; when grown, they will also feed on rock fish and even six-foot conger eels.

CREATURES OF THE ROCKY COASTS

The grey seal is limited to a narrow belt across the North Atlantic. It does not range as far as the ice-fields of the north, nor, on the other hand, does it continue south into the milder temperate regions. Instead, it haunts the rockbound coasts and outlying islands on both sides of the Atlantic at latitudes of southern Canada and Great Britain, where the sea is deep and the rough, troubled waters are rarely still.

Grey is of course the dominant colour of this species, but individuals may vary from almost black to pale tints, often blotched with irregular splashes of darker tones. The grey seal is about the size of a harp seal; large males measure a good eight feet and weigh about six hundred pounds.

Though the grey seal may make extended cruises at sea, it generally remains in the neighbourhood of the ancestral breeding grounds; in fact, a few members of the colony stay close by those rocky places the year round.

BEARDED SEALS—GIANTS OF THE ARCTIC

The Bearded Seal, *Erignathus barbatus*, gets its name from the festoons of coarse, flattened bristles that hang from each side of its mouth. (Sealers have another name for this species—they call it the "square flipper", after the characteristic shape of the limbs.) The animal is one of the largest of the northern varieties: the male bearded seal is ten or twelve feet long and weighs in the neighbourhood of eight hundred pounds. Now and then we come across a giant that may reach fifteen hundred pounds. Females are about seven feet in length and weigh much less than the males.

Dwelling on the shore ice in the North Atlantic and Arctic regions, the bearded seal is more or less solitary, often living alone or in small family groups. The pelt is of little value in the fur trade, but is esteemed by the Eskimos for the extra-thick hide, which they cut up for harpoon lines and other heavy-duty gear.

Discord among walruses arises chiefly from their dislike of being disturbed while sleeping. In such close quarters one will accidentally
nudge another, and the offended sleeper with a mighty roar slaps its
nearest neighbour, setting off a chain reaction that quickly has the
entire colony in bellowing turmoil.   *See page 608*

[5-15]

[5-15A]

The California sea lion is the ''trained seal''
familiar to circus and zoo goers. Its small
external ears and rotating hind flippers
distinguish it from the true seal
See page 605

[5-16]

The numerous species of eared seals or sea lions vary greatly in colour. Their young, born on land, must be taught to swim, but from the age of six or eight weeks they are at home in the water.
See page 600

True seals, being more highly specialized for life in the water, do not have external ears, and their hind flippers extend straight out behind them. Covered with short coarse hair, they lack the commercially valuable underfur of the eared seals, but are slaughtered by the thousand for leather and oil. *See page 612*

[5-16A]

More Animal Friends and Helpers

Cats

SEEING IN THE DARK

THE ability of cats to see well in the dark, long ago gave them a touch of the macabre. People came to associate them with the night time activities of witches and hobgoblins, particularly on Hallow-e'en. Because of this reputation, children are especially interested to know just how cats' eyes function.

At the back of the eye is a reflecting surface which catches and reflects any available bit of light. The resulting glow enables the cat to see in situations where our eyes are inadequate. The startling green glare given off by a cat's eyes is due to this reflection, its eye being almost completely covered by the pupil. During the day the pupil is narrowed down to a mere slit. In adult cats the iris is usually yellow; in kittens it may be blue or green.

SENSITIVE FEELERS

Cats, like dogs, have moist noses, and their senses of smell and hearing are keen. The hairs in a cat's ears, far from being obstructions, are sensitive aids in catching sounds. Cats can detect vibrations beyond the range of the human ear. They are often critical of musical performances, removing themselves as far as possible from shrill radio music or singing practice in the home.

The hairs on a cat's face—its whiskers—are also valuable as "feelers". A set of whiskers contains between twenty-five and thirty hairs. If you look at them closely, you will note that they are set in four lines above and at the sides of the mouth, where they are connected to sensitive nerves. Feelers are useful to hunters, especially night hunters, as Pussy is when in its natural state; the hairs supply information about the underbrush or other terrain through which the animal is moving.

THE CAT AS A HUNTER

Stalking and pouncing on prey come as naturally to a cat as breathing. Where the dog uses sheer power and speed, the cat resorts to stealth and cunning. Having discovered the haunts of a possible victim, the cat crouches motionless until the right instant to spring. The weight of the marauder's body knocks down the rabbit, mouse, or other victim—which the cat then seizes with its sharp hooked claws and its strong canine teeth to make the kill.

If you look into Pussy's mouth you can see the equipment of a real prowler of the jungle. There are two big sharp tushes in each jaw. Its molars are sharp-edged wedges, perfectly adapted for cutting up meat. Its tongue is so rough it can rasp juices from meat.

CATS ARE MODEL MOTHERS

It is a rare cat mother that shirks her responsibility to her kittens. As a rule, even before they are born she shows her solicitude by looking for a dark secluded spot for their entrance into the world—just as in the primitive state a cat sought a dark cave for the event. Though kittens are active almost immediately after birth, they do not start to open their eyes until after five days or so. Within ten days the eyes are fully open.

Meanwhile the mother nurses the kittens and industriously washes them from nose-tip to tail with her rough tongue. She allows them to romp and play boisterously—even to the extent of frolicking over and around her; but if they go too far she will box their ears soundly.

When they are older she gives them lessons in hunting, if circumstances permit, showing all the tricks at her command for catching mice and other prey. She will even instruct them in the fine art of backing down a tree trunk—an important accomplishment for a cat. Instinct prompts cats to climb, but many a cat that has had no coaching may reach the top of a tree and then be too terrified to descend. Often the fire brigade must come to the rescue!

CHILDREN AND CATS

When a cat—and this is even truer of a kitten—is brought into the home, training is usually desirable in more than one respect. Not only must we teach the little animal how to fit into the family programme; we also need to instruct the children of the family how to handle and treat their pet.

A frightened cat or one that has been excited or angered by teasing, may inflict serious scratches on a child. It is not difficult to teach even a small child to pick up a cat properly—by approaching it from the back or side and placing one arm under the cat's forelegs and the other around its body underneath the abdomen. The best way to pick up a little kitten is by placing your hand under its body. Grasping the scruff of its neck will not hurt a cat, but it is not a sensation that the animal enjoys; it is best to resort to it only for disciplinary reasons.

CAT LANGUAGE

Children will quickly learn something of the cat's own language: the happy purr, the soft mew of contentment, the begging miaow of hunger, the frightened yowl, the shrill battle cry when the cat is involved in a fight. The cat's body is just as expressive as its voice. A lashing tail (in contrast to a dog's happy wag) is a sign of angry excitement. At such times the cat's ears lie back—and if it is badly frightened, its hair stands on end over its entire body and tail.

WHERE CATS CAME FROM

Though we can trace back the cat family millions of years to prehistoric times, there is much about the ancestry of domestic cats that remains a mystery. Many conflicting theories have been advanced from time to time regarding their origin.

The striped tabby pattern is a strong indication that the forebear of our pets of today was either the European wildcat or the African wildcat, for both of these species have a striped pattern. But which of the two was the original ancestor is a question that has been hotly debated. The most generally held opinion favours the African or Kaffir cat, which was tamed by the ancient Egyptians. For centuries the domestic short-hair cats have mated haphazardly, and as a result there is more variation in their size and form than in any other breeds.

PERSIAN CATS

The Persian, or long-hair, cat is generally believed to have originated somewhere in East Asia. Though its long silky coat and fluffy tail give the Persian infinite grace, it is not so lithe in build as the short-hair cats. Its body and legs are both short and compact. "Refined" seems the most suitable adjective for the Persian. It is characteristically unaggressive, lofty in its bearing, and has a soft, well-modulated voice.

SIAMESE CATS

The Siamese cat is a comparative newcomer to America, the first of the breed having been imported from England little more than fifty years ago. Only a few years before that a famous pair named Pho and Mia were first brought to England from Siam. The Siamese cat is distinguished by its form—its hind legs, being longer than the front ones, give the body a slight tilt upward from the shoulder to pelvis, and its head is long and wedge-shaped with a flat forehead.

The Siamese cat also has a peculiar coloration, which varies with three distinctive types. The seal point Siamese has cream or fawn-coloured body fur, with face, ears, legs, and tail a seal brown. Its slanted eyes are a deep sapphire blue. In the blue point Siamese, the body colour may be cream or pale blue with the points (or markings) a deeper blue. As for the chocolate Siamese, it has a deeper body tone and rich brown markings.

The acrobatic ability of Siamese cats, combined with their great mischievousness, gave rise to the legend that their ancestry was part monkey. The legend is completely fanciful, but it is amusing to recall it as you watch a Siamese climbing, leaping, twisting its tail and in general performing tricks.

THE MANX

One of the oddities of animal life is the Manx—a cat without a tail! This breed, whose ancestors hailed from the Isle of Man in the Irish Sea, has a particularly mild and trusting nature and as a pet is especially easy to train and manage.

Pet Shows and Pictures

Once your children are interested in the different breeds of cats and dogs, attending a pet show becomes a worthwhile family excursion. At such an exhibition you can see fine specimens of many breeds and observe the fascinating results of specialized training. If you live in a neighbourhood where a number of children own dogs and cats, it is possible to stage a strictly home-style pet show guaranteed to provide fun as well as an added incentive for the young masters and mistresses to have their pets well groomed and trained.

Making a cat or dog picture album is an activity anyone can enjoy. It is fun to watch the magazines for suitable pictures, and even the youngest member of the family can join in the game. The resulting album can be either extremely simple or else elaborate, depending on the amount of time you can give as adviser to the "art and production department".

Horses

If there was ever the possibility of a waning of interest in horses in this machine age of ours, that prospect vanished when television brought Western movies with their hard-riding cowboys into the home. Life on a ranch with horses became the dream of countless city-dwelling girls and boys, and children who had the opportunity to ride felt a new appreciation of that privilege.

Fortunately it is not necessary to live on a ranch to have a personal acquaintance with horses. There are some farms where we still may see different breeds of horses, and horse shows are held throughout the country. In some cities there are the magnificent steeds of mounted police, as well as riding horses in the parks. In at least a few communities, the plodding horse of the milkman still survives.

HORSEBACK RIDING

A resident of a large city had a young daughter who regularly "galloped" rather than walked along the street. This was a real worry to her parents, as the girl had a heart condition which ruled out strenuous activity. After many attempts to dissuade her, her mother happened to ask *why* she galloped. Her daughter's answer was a matter-of-fact: "I'm riding my horse." Mother and doctor then got together on the happy solution of providing limited riding lessons which actually benefited the girl's health.

When a boy or girl is given an opportunity to ride, an understanding of the background of the horse is genuinely valuable; for some of the animal's qualities and reactions are easily traceable to its wild ancestors. When startled, a horse shies in the way a wild horse would from a suddenly discovered enemy. The wise rider, therefore, speaks in a confident and encouraging voice to his shying horse instead of scolding or hitting him.

When a horse lays his ears flat back, it is a warning that he is angry. The ears may also be an indication of a horse's character. The horse with ears drooped or turned back is likely to be treacherous, whereas quick-moving ears are a sign of a particularly sensitive nature. A good horse has ears pointed upward or forward. He also has a broad space between the eyes, and his head is high between the ears.

A HORSE'S TEETH TELL ITS AGE

The child who feeds a horse discovers that it is wise to offer lumps of sugar in an open palm rather than grasped in his finger tips. A horse can crop grass even more closely than a cow, thanks to his large incisor teeth. These teeth might easily nip the fingers with the sugar.

It is by these incisors that an experienced horseman can estimate the age of a horse. As the teeth develop, annual growth rings are formed in them. (The effect is somewhat like that of growth rings in a tree trunk.) As the teeth wear with age, these rings become clearly visible. The time-honoured warning not to look a gift horse in the mouth is based on this revelation of the animal's age by the state of its teeth.

Behind the incisors is a bare space which allows for the placing of a bit, and behind this are six molars on each side of each jaw. When a male horse is about three years old, canine teeth appear behind the incisors—four in all. In a mare these canines are generally small or completely missing.

HOW HORSES RUN

Would-be cowboys and cowgirls thrill to the pounding of hoofs as horses gallop across the plains. They may notice that during a gallop the horse is completely off the ground for a moment after each spring forward. The animal makes each spring from one of his fore feet and lands on the hind foot of the opposite side of his body. Just before this "pair" of feet touches the earth the other two are coming up again, so that the body is in the air with all legs bent beneath.

When a horse is walking, two or more of his feet are always on the ground. The order of their progression is right hind foot, right fore foot, left hind foot, left fore foot. In a canter the same rotation of feet is used, but the motion is of course much more rapid. When the horse trots, each diagonal pair of legs is alternately raised and put forward.

THE HORSE'S WILD RELATIVES

A well-groomed horse is sleek, glossy, and thoroughly "civilized" in appearance, but an animal that has been running in the pasture all winter long presents a very different picture. Like all wild horses, which grow a thick covering of hair during cold weather, he has a shaggy coat. They shed this hair in the springtime.

Wild horses still exist in limited numbers. These include the so-called tarpans of Mongolia and Central Asia, which, though smaller than domesticated horses, are strong and of stocky build.

There are still herds of half-wild horses on America's western prairies—descendants from horses brought to Mexico by Cortez and to Florida by De Soto. Some of these imports from Spain strayed from their masters and roamed far and wide over the new continent. Eventually members of the two groups met and mated, and before long thousands of unbridled horses added a colourful note to the American scene. Comparatively few survive in the wild state today; and of this remnant, many are captured by ranch owners, branded, and then released. We generally speak of these animals as "mustangs".

As for "bronco", this is not a name for a special breed, but rather a generic term applied to any wild American horse that is captured and trained for man's use. Today's broncos are usually born of domesticated horses, then turned loose and allowed to run wild until they reach the age of usefulness.

The African zebras, members of the horse family, have resisted all attempts to domesticate them. By way of contrast Shetland ponies, which still run wild in the Shetland Islands and other islands north of Scotland, are valuable pack animals and trustworthy pets and riding ponies for children.

WHERE HORSES CAME FROM

The distribution of horses in the modern world follows a long history of wanderings and migrations. The family started in North America with the "Dawn Horse"—the original ancestor. This was a creature about the size of a fox, with several toes on each foot. Over a long period of time gradual changes took place in later ancestral horses, notably in the lengthening of the legs and the steady enlargement and greater specialization of the middle toe. At the same time the other toes grew smaller and smaller, finally vanishing and being replaced by the enormously enlarged middle toe, which had taken on the proportions of the hoof as we know it today.

Even before the Ice Age, some of the ancestral horses had been leaving North America for other continents, and the true horse of the Ice Age migrated also. Then, while the branches that had gone to Asia, Europe and Africa flourished, the original North American family died out. Thus there were no horses on the North American continent until the Spanish explorers brought them back.

THOROUGHBREDS AND OTHER POPULAR BREEDS

Even when many groups of horses still lived in the wild state, men in diverse lands were busy breeding the animals for specialized uses. To these efforts we owe such breeds as the German coach horse, the Belgian saddle horse, the American saddle horse. Especially notable breeds were developed in England, among them the thoroughbred, which became so famous as a horse of high quality that people began to use the term incorrectly, saying "thoroughbred" when they meant "purebred". (A purebred animal is one which has known and recorded ancestry and represents but one breed.)

Thoroughbreds excel in running, and the finest race horses are of this breed. All our thoroughbreds nowadays are descended from three horses brought to England more than two hundred years ago—two of them Arabian steeds, the remaining one Turkish.

Arabian Horses. Originally Arabian horses were creatures of the desert and, as such, needed little food and water. So great was the dependence of the Arabs hundreds of years ago on their horses that they bred the animals with great care, raised them virtually as members of the family, and trained them like children. The result after several generations was one of the most remarkable triumphs of domestication —a truly great breed, outstanding in appearance, intelligence and performance. Not the least value of the Arabian horse lies in its contribution to new breeds—the thoroughbred, for example.

THE HUMBLE DONKEY AND MULE

Children know donkeys as amusingly stubborn creatures. Though these relatives of the horse often do display a rather difficult temperament, they are valuable as beasts of burden in arid regions, and for the breeding of mules (a mule being the offspring of a male donkey and a mare). Donkeys are descended from wild asses which were tamed and used in Egypt before the horse became domesticated. In its size, short hair and other less noticeable features, an ass bears a closer resemblance to the zebra than to the horse. It even has a tendency to show stripes on the legs.

Mules are larger than donkeys, and shaped more like horses. Still, with their long ears, small hoofs, and large heads, they rather resemble donkeys. They are also considered valuable as pack animals, being noted for their sureness of foot and their great powers of endurance. As a rule, they cannot reproduce their kind.

Cattle

About the first things a toddler learns about cattle is that cows say "Moo", and that cows give milk. The cow thereupon becomes an impressive figure, milk being the most important and most frequent item in a child's diet. Even a child of five is more likely than not to tell you gravely that "milk gives vitamins". His older brother is interested in cows too—but mainly because they are the pawns in our televised folklore of ranchers and rustlers.

COWS FOR MILK

Man has developed all the varieties of domesticated cattle from wild species of Asia and Europe. It took many generations of selective breeding to achieve such marvels as the Holstein cow, which can produce its weight in milk in two weeks, and the Jersey, which gives more than five thousand pounds of rich milk in a year! Other noted dairy breeds are the Guernsey, Ayrshire, and brown Swiss cows.

There are certain features by which you can recognize a good milch cow. These include: the head high between the eyes, which should be clear, large, and placid; a large mouth with a muscular lower jaw; a deep wide chest, hips much broader than the shoulders, and a large, well-supported abdomen. As you would expect, the udder should be large and its four quarters of equal size.

CATTLE FOR BEEF

Apart from the cattle bred for milk production there are the breeds designed as beef factories. Among the best known of these are the Hereford, Aberdeen-Angus, Galloway, and Shorthorn. You can see many contrasts between them and the milch cows. The beef cattle are big and full across the back and have thick, short necks. (You will notice that the milch cow has a thin, fine neck.) The shape of the body is markedly different in these groups. The milch cow's body is oval and the outline of her body sags in front of the hips, whereas the meat animal tends more to a square-shaped body and its back is straight from neck to tail.

HOW MILK IS PRODUCED

Most city children do not see cows very often, so it is not surprising that they develop some strange notions about how cows give milk. For one thing, the supply of milk seems as constant as water flowing from a tap. Another misconception has turned up since the homogenizing process became widespread; many children believe that milk is originally produced in that state. And I am probably not the only one who has heard a small child wondering what kind of cows give *chocolate* milk!

Despite the way in which man has disrupted the animal's natural processes, a cow still produces milk as nourishment for her own offspring. Her supply of milk is of course most abundant soon after a calf is born. Under normal conditions she would go dry as soon as the young one could turn to other feeds, but a domestic cow that is milked continuously may give milk for almost a year. The quantity decreases, however, after six to eight months, and the cow must be bred again to renew the milk supply. A wise dairy-farmer does not expect cows to produce constantly, and gives them a rest of at least six weeks every year.

HOW COWS EAT

If your child watches a horse and cow grazing, he may observe as he looks on that the horse is pulling his head in whereas the cow is pushing her head forward. These distinctive eating habits are no accident; they are determined by each animal's mouth and teeth formations.

A cow has eight front teeth on her lower jaw, with only a horny pad above them. While grazing, she runs her tongue out, seizes a clump of grass, and closes her upper lip tightly over it. A forward thrust of her head then causes the teeth below to cut or tear the grass from its roots. Thus she always eats "away from herself".

The horse cannot gather grass with his tongue, but he can use his flexible upper lip to grasp it. He has both upper and lower teeth and, taking the grass between these two rows, he cuts it by pulling his head back. Thus a horse always eats "towards himself".

There is another striking difference in the eating habits of horses and cows. A horse chews as it grazes. The cow uses a different technique, due to the fact that instead of one stomach, she has four! She swallows the grass exactly as it is cut, and the unchewed food goes directly into her first stomach. Later the food progresses to the second stomach, where it is formed into cud balls in a convenient size for chewing. When the cow lies down, this food is brought back to the mouth. She chews her cud contentedly with her grinding teeth until it is ready to be swallowed. It then passes to her third and fourth stomachs, where it is digested.

Mammals equipped to eat in this fashion are known as ruminants. They include sheep, deer, antelope, and camels. In the wild state, the ruminants' technique is a definite protection, for they can graze rapidly in the open (where flesh-eating beasts might prey upon them), and then retire to a sheltered area to continue their meal in comparative safety.

HOW CATTLE EXPRESS THEMSELVES

Though their domestication goes back through countless generations, cattle still reveal traces of their wild ancestry. Their vocal expressions are akin to those of cattle still living in the wild state. The bull gives a sullen roar when he is angry. The cow moos gently to her calf, and the lowing sound so characteristic of late afternoon in dairy farm country is the call of the herd—the call which kept members of a group together when they were in the natural state.

Though the adult cow gives the impression of being the most phlegmatic of creatures, few animals are more frolicsome than a calf. Even cows sometimes forget their dignity, kicking up their heels exuberantly as the tail is held aloft. In bulls the instinct for battle is still strong. Those living in the wild state use their vicious horns not so much against other animals as against rival bulls that attempt to displace them as master of a harem.

GOOD HEARERS AND SMELLERS

Cattle have a keen sense of hearing, benefiting from the fact that they can turn their ears in any direction. Their sense of smell is also excellent. The moist, sensitive nose is equally well adapted for picking up the scent of an enemy or deciding if food is properly edible.

TAIL-SWITCHING

As the cow is such an emphatic tail switcher, an observer might read into the action those meanings which apply to the tail movements of a dog or cat. However, the tail has nothing to do with a cow's emotions; it is an efficient fly-brush and swatter, and without it a cow would be miserably at the mercy of these ubiquitous insects.

Goats—They Don't Eat Cans

Children are usually amused as well as impressed by the fact that goats will eat anything, but one young girl I know was more impressed than amused. Lying on the grass reading one fine afternoon, she was so absorbed in her story that she paid no attention to a gentle tugging at her braided hair. Suddenly she realized that a goat was thoughtfully chewing one of the braids!

This seemingly fantastic willingness to "try anything once" in the way of food begins to make more sense when a child realizes that in the wild state goats must subsist on the most meagre resources. As moss, lichens, and bits of vegetation are the best fare to be found high on the rocky mountain slopes where goats live, it is hardly surprising that they are not very "choosy" about what they introduce to their digestive systems. There is a popular fallacy that goats eat tin cans. What they really enjoy eating is the glue from the paper labels on the cans.

GOATS ARE USEFUL ANIMALS

By means of selective breeding, man has developed goats to serve him in more ways than one. He uses the Angora and Cashmere for their hair, which is woven into very fine fabrics. Another type, the short-hair goat, yields a good meat supply, and still another group is valued for its milk.

These three kinds of goats have served people all over the world, and today milk goats are found in every part of the United States. Many belong to commercial dairies, but probably half of them are "back yard" residents. A great point in their favour is that they can eke out an existence even when the food supply is at its scantiest.

Goat's milk is superior to cow's milk for two reasons. Goat's milk is digested more quickly and completely, and it is safe without pasteurization. Its taste, slightly different from that of cow's milk, is preferred by some people but is displeasing to others. Goats do not get tuberculosis and they are as nearly disease-free as any domestic animal.

A goat becomes an affectionate pet if it is well treated. When a goat is angry, it shows its feelings by shaking its head. It defends itself by butting with its head and striking an adversary with its sharp horns.

Sheep—They Came Down from Mountains

Like goats, sheep are mountain animals. Even when they are domesticated they thrive best in cool dry surroundings. In the wild state they lived in less rough localities than mountain goats do, but on the other hand sheep were able to subsist on pasturage that was too thin for cattle.

The sheep's great wool coat, originally developed as a protection against cold, has been particularly exploited in the Merino breed of Spain which produces exceptionally fine wool. In England, where mutton is a staple food, such breeds as the Dorset and Shropshire are valued for their flesh, although their wool is also used to good advantage.

OBEDIENCE SAVES THE SHEEP

Most children are familiar with the figure of speech that puts people blindly following a leader on the same level with "a lot of sheep". This scornful phrase implies that the unquestioning obedience indicates a lack of intelligence; yet in the case of sheep the instinct for following has often saved their lives.

When sheep lived in the wild state, they gathered habitually in flocks to feed, with a sentinel always on guard. When this leader spied an approaching enemy or picked up his scent, he signalled with a bleat of alarm, then started off with the whole flock immediately at his heels. Over difficult terrain, leaping from precipices when necessary, leader and flock made their way until they reached a safe retreat.

The bleating sound for which sheep are noted is their means of keeping in touch with each other. In time of danger they are silent; but they have a special bleat when they catch sight of an enemy and another one when they come upon water.

Sheep have keen senses. Their large ears move alertly toward the direction of any sound. They can pick up the faintest scent. Their excellent eyes alter according to the light conditions. In sunshine the eye is just a narrow slit, showing a yellowish or brownish iris; in a dim light the pupil grows larger until it absorbs practically the whole eye.

HOW SHEEP FEED

The teeth of sheep and goats are alike. There are six rear grinding teeth on each side of the upper and lower jaws, and eight incisors on the lower but none on the upper. Thus equipped, sheep can crop short grass close to its roots. Because the close cropping by sheep may ruin pasture and because sheep droppings render grass obnoxious to cattle, sheep herders and cattlemen have had bitter conflicts in some countries. In any event, sheep and goats manage to be well fed where cattle might starve. Man probably could not invent a more efficient self-powered lawn mower!

Pigs—Smarter Than You Think

"*Dirty* pig!" exclaims the tot just learning the names of animals.

It is a pity that pigs' habits are so generally misunderstood, for actually pigs are in fact amongst the most intelligent, valuable, and interesting of domesticated mammals. The notion that they enjoy filthy surroundings is largely the consequence of man's carelessness in keeping them.

The truth is that a pig will keep its own bed clean and neat under the most discouraging conditions. The wild hogs of India, for example, make themselves quite respectable nests which resemble grass huts— thatched on top and with openings at the side.

The fact that pigs like to wallow in mud is advanced as further evidence that they like dirt. The real reason for their wallowing is that the pig, being only sparsely covered with hairs and bristles, is a constant victim of flies and other insects. It has no tail, as a cow has, to swish these tormentors off, and so its only hope of cleaning itself free of pests is to take a mud bath.

Your child probably shares the general view that the pig's nose is singularly ugly. Be that as it may, the nose has many uses and is even comparable to the elephant's trunk in its value to its owner. The fleshy covering of the nostrils is a sensitive feeling-organ which, especially in the wilds, aids the pig to locate bulbs, acorns, roots, and other foods. Besides guiding the pig to food, the nose also serves as a digging tool. Bony plates under the flesh give it remarkable strength.

"Pig eyes", small but gleaming, reflect a good brain, though tame pigs rarely have a chance to show how intelligent they are. Wild pigs have large open ears; those of tame breeds vary, some being sharp and forward-opening, others lopped. The distinctive feature of the male pig's teeth is the upward curve of its upper canines. These tusks, especially in the wild boar, make formidable weapons.

PIG TALK

Though the squeals and grunts of a pig are anything but musical, they are interestingly intelligible to the human ear. You recognize the hunger squeal easily enough by its querulous tone, and the terrified squeal of fright is equally unmistakable. It does not take you long to distinguish between the grunt of well-fed satisfaction and the habitual grunting that echoes wild animal ways. Continuous grunting was once the means by which the pig herd kept together.